CONCRETE MIX DESIGN

To

PATSY

CONCRETE MIX DESIGN

F. D. LYDON

B.E., M.Phil. (Lond.), C.Eng., M.I.C.E., M.I. Mun. E.

Department of Civil Engineering and Building Technology
University of Wales Institute of Science and Technology
Cardiff

APPLIED SCIENCE PUBLISHERS LTD

LONDON

APPLIED SCIENCE PUBLISHERS LTD
RIPPLE ROAD, BARKING, ESSEX, ENGLAND

ISBN: 0 85334 552 X

WITH 37 ILLUSTRATIONS AND 22 TABLES

REPRINTED 1979

Printed in Great Britain by Galliard Limited, Great Yarmouth, Norfolk, England

PREFACE

The view is sometimes expressed that concrete mix design data, presented as being applicable to typical materials representative of their kind, are not very helpful and, indeed, are of little practical value. A different, and more alarming opinion, must be held by those who, full of awesome confidence, produce precise mix proportions, with impeccable arithmetic, convinced of the authoritative accuracy of tabulated and graphical data and serenely untroubled by trial mixes.

There is some truth in the former view; anyone sufficiently practised in the art of mix design can be expected to support this logically. For him the principles are self-evident, and soundly based intuitive choices which are difficult to explain scientifically, are nevertheless rational and deductive. The proof of this is in the success with which the optimum combination of materials is chosen and that, after all, is the proper criterion by which any mix design process is judged.

The alarm engendered by the uncritical confidence in published data is realistic and justified; there has always been (as there also has in the field of structural design) an unfortunate tendency in some engineers to confuse successful operations on data with successful design; it is not unknown for a designer to insist that, where actual performance fails to coincide with that predicted, the former is somehow wrong and the latter correct, despite the assumptions and idealisations built into the prediction theory!

This monograph is intended to help those who need mix design placed in perspective and those who are looking for guidance. It is not a new approach—this is not likely until a major, fundamental breakthrough occurs—and generally aims at presenting existing data in, it is hoped, a helpful and practical way. Some aspects of available information are given less prominence than is usual, or even omitted, on the grounds that experience over many years has shown this to be justified.

To assist in the attempt to utilise mix design fully it is considered desirable to sketch in some background on the fresh and hardened concrete; this is, of necessity here, very limited in scope but sufficient to point to the principles underlying the choice of mix proportions and subsequent modification thereof. Most of the useful conventional approaches to mix proportioning are included; it is impossible to be objective, of course, and others will probably prefer a different set. However, many years of practising, discussing and attempted teaching of the mix design process have led to this particular monograph, written as a brief introduction towards satisfying an apparent need.

Grateful acknowledgement is made to the many authors whose work is quoted and particularly to the Cement and Concrete Association for the opportunities afforded while working there on concrete technology.

CONTENTS

CHAPTER 3

THE PROPERTIES OF HARDENED CONCRETE

CHAPTER 4

THE ROAD NOTE NO. 4 METHOD OF MIX DESIGN

CHAPTER 5

METHODS OF COMBINING AGGREGATES TO OBTAIN DESIRED GRADINGS

CHAPTER 6

GAP-GRADED CONCRETE

CHAPTER 7

MIX DESIGN FOR HIGH STRENGTH CONCRETE

CHAPTER 8

MIX DESIGN FOR AIR-ENTRAINED CONCRETE

CHAPTER 9

LIGHTWEIGHT AGGREGATE CONCRETE

CHAPTER 10

MIX DESIGN FOR TENSILE STRENGTH

CHAPTER 11

THE USE OF STATISTICS IN MIX DESIGN

Chapter 1

BACKGROUND TO MIX DESIGN

1.1 INTRODUCTION

Considerable study, particularly in the last twenty to thirty years, has led to a much better understanding of the structure and behaviour of concrete. This has been accompanied by an improved and more sophisticated technology and the product now made, in its variety of forms, is much more capable of satisfying the increasingly stringent demands required of it. The criteria normally explicitly demanded are, for many reasons (some of which are dealt with in Chapters 2 and 3), rather simple, although the underlying desirable behaviour is quite complex.

Because the behaviour of both fresh and hardened concrete is significantly related to their composition it should be possible, at least in principle, to choose the latter to provide satisfaction in the former. This is mix design; it is the choosing of the ingredients to provide, economically, concrete possessing desired properties. It implies the deliberate proportioning of cement, fine and coarse aggregates and water, taking account of not only the specified concrete properties but also the characteristics of the specific materials used.

1.2 NOMINAL MIXES

The widespread use of concrete as a construction material necessitated rationalisation of the design and production process and eventually led to the use of mixes of fixed proportions which generally ensured that concrete of adequate strength was made. These mixes had the virtue of simplicity and, under normal circumstances, had a comforting margin of strength above that specified. However, they took no account of materials of varying characteristics and thus were sometimes much too rich in cement content and yet were sometimes not rich enough.

These nominal mixes had, typically, aggregate/cement ratios of 3:1, 4·5:1 and 6:1, by volume proportion.[1] As long as aggregates were batched by volume, proportioning by volume was reasonable; but conversion to weight proportions was required for weigh-batching and this led to ambiguities because of the choice of bulk density measurements available. (A 6:1 mix by volume might be 6·2:1 by weight if dry, loose bulk density data were used, or 6·7:1 if dry, compacted bulk density data were accepted.)

A rather widespread rigidity regarding the fine/coarse aggregate ratio added considerably to the problems associated with nominal mixes, but subsequent relaxation of the 1:2 proportions led to improvements and allowed a wider range of materials to be used satisfactorily. Ratios of from about 1:3 to about 1:1 (fine:coarse aggregate) were frequently accepted, but lack of understanding of the need for this adjustment by very many users of concrete still caused practical difficulties.

1.3 STANDARD MIXES

The publication of CP 116[2] in 1965 introduced a set of mixes which were specified in terms of dry weights of aggregates per bag of cement, which displaced nominal mixes and which allowed flexibility in terms of types of aggregate used, degree of workability chosen and level of quality control exercised on site. These standard mixes are, by definition, conservative (in terms of cement content), but are useful, 'off the shelf' sets of proportions that allow the desired concrete to be produced with the minimum of preparatory work. They avoid the ambiguities of the nominal mixes and are more relevant to present materials.

1.4 DESIGNED MIXES

The most rational approach to the selection of mix proportions is to choose them with specific materials in mind, possessing characteristics more or less unique to themselves, by virtue of which concrete with the appropriate properties is most economically produced. This is not a practical reality and the approach is very much one of compromise.

Materials have been broadly categorised into convenient groups (*e.g.* normal Portland cements are generally taken as ordinary or rapid-hardening; aggregates may be termed rounded, irregular or angular in particle shape) and useful relationships have been established between sets of variables for materials typical of these groups. These data then allow mix proportions to be selected which, if the ingredients were perfectly typical, would produce the correct concrete.

The essence of the procedure is thus:

Hardened concrete— (strength, durability)	type of cement age of concrete	→ water/cement ratio
Fresh concrete— (workability)	water/cement ratio aggregate characteristics	→ aggregate/cement ratio

Figure 1.1 shows the process graphically.

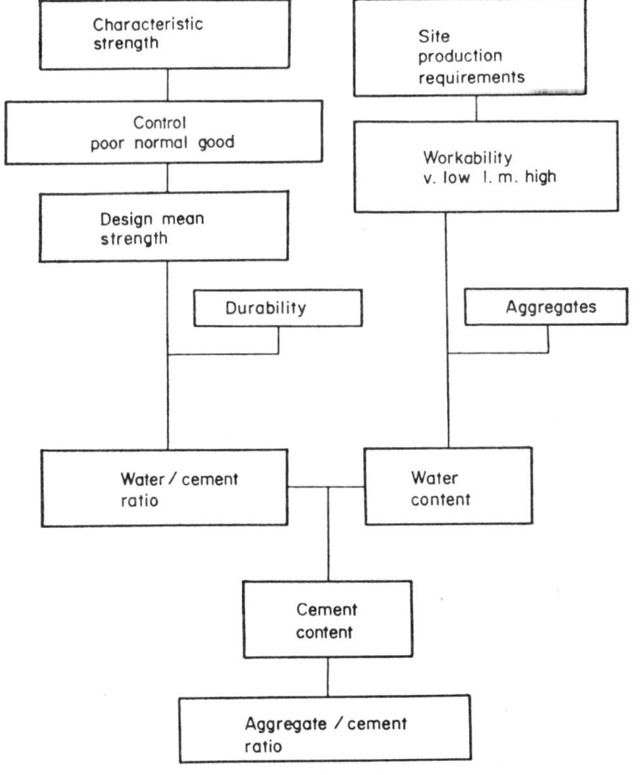

FIG. 1.1 The mix design process.

Naturally the data used do not strictly apply to the specific materials used in a particular mix and, consequently, it is unlikely that the resultant behaviour will be entirely satisfactory. Indeed, it will frequently be found to be very unsatisfactory, but with experience considerable success can be achieved! This means, therefore, that being arithmetically correct in the use of the data does not guarantee the correct concrete mix; trial mixes are essential. A number of subjective decisions are required on which hinge important ramifications for the concrete; they require much skill and judgement and preclude merely the use of published data as the sole means of mix proportioning.

1.5 PRIORITIES

It should be noted that while there are, of course, many occasions on which it is necessary or desirable to go through the process of mix design—for example, for large volumes of concrete where minimising cement content may have large financial benefits; or where, for technical reasons, the type of concrete required or the particular criteria specified necessitate careful selection and proportioning of ingredients—there should be benefits accruing therefrom, otherwise the exercise need hardly be undertaken. Much ordinary concrete is used, from which quite undemanding performance is specified and for which the cost of mix design would hardly be recovered. The use of standard mixes, or even of nominal mixes (however archaic and unfashionable they may be thought), is quite acceptable in such cases. Mix design for its own sake may be interesting but not profitable; it should be practised only where necessary.

Chapter 2

THE PROPERTIES OF PLASTIC CONCRETE

2.1 INTRODUCTION

Concrete in the plastic state must have certain characteristics if it is to allow the hardened concrete to achieve its full potential. Without these desirable properties the strength, deformation, density, water-tightness, durability, appearance and other properties will be adversely affected. It is therefore necessary to ensure that the plastic concrete is suitable from the point of view of handling, placing and finishing and to recognise the factors affecting a change in such behaviour.

Between them two properties cover all that is required of the freshly mixed concrete; they are (a) workability and (b) stability. Both are essentially 'practical' properties and are therefore intuitive to everyone dealing with concrete production. However, each is highly complex and not easily, precisely defined; it follows that we cannot easily measure them in absolute terms and this means that any results obtained are specific to the test we have used. We need not be too alarmed about this since the practical concrete technologist, although interested in fundamentals, is *primarily* concerned with effects rather than causes; he wants to know what relative change takes place as a result of certain factors and not an absolute measure of the change. So we can proceed by adopting some functional, but necessarily incomplete, definition of these properties, endeavour to measure them, allocate orders of value to them, for concretes suitable for different uses, and ascertain the factors affecting their behaviour. We can, therefore, establish the relative suitabilities of concretes of different mix proportions.

2.2 WORKABILITY

There have been many attempts at defining this, notably by Glanville *et al.*[3] and Stewart.[4] Most definitions are really relevant to compactability rather than workability and, of course, this is natural since the former is relatively easily measured. If we accept this term as being of practical significance we may say that the compactability of concrete is a measure of the amount of work to be done on the concrete, under standard conditions, to achieve full compaction. The higher the compactability the less work is required; the lower the compactability the greater the work required. We must be careful to stipulate 'under standard conditions' otherwise what we are trying to measure would not only be a function of the concrete, but also of the mould into which it was being compacted, the method of compaction, the amount of reinforcement, and so on. For example, suppose we have a mix which has a 6:1 aggregate/cement ratio with 40% sand and a certain amount of water. We check the compactability by placing this concrete into an unreinforced road slab and intensely vibrating it by means of an oscillating heavy beam. We conclude that the compactability is very good. Subsequently we use a similar concrete in a heavily reinforced, narrow wall section; because we now have difficulty in compacting it—using external vibrators—we conclude that the compactability is very poor. But the concrete has not changed. Thus we have the same concrete with quite different compactabilities. Had we used the same means of compacting and the same moulds on each occasion we would have found that the compactabilities were the same; had we changed the mix proportions in one case this would have yielded a different answer because the concrete *would* be different. We must therefore standardise our test conditions.

Since it is conventional to refer to 'workability' we shall do so from now on, rather than keep referring to compactability. For practical purposes we shall lose little in doing so.

2.3 MEASURING WORKABILITY

Numerous tests have been devised for this purpose but three are of particular interest. They are (a) the slump test, (b) the compacting factor test and (c) the 'V–B' consistometer test. These three cover almost the whole history of 'modern' concrete technology—spanning about forty years—and are now standard tests covered by BS 1881,[5] which gives complete details.

2.3.1 The slump test

This is the oldest and most widely used test on site. The standard form suffers from the disadvantage that it is virtually impossible to lift the cone vertically at the end of the test and thus it is easy to tilt the concrete cone, thereby affecting the result. A modified apparatus overcomes this difficulty by having a vertical column rigidly fixed to the non-absorbent base plate and a grooved attachment to the slump cone which slides up and down the column. The cone can be lifted vertically only and there is no danger of tilting.

It is imperative that the correct procedure be followed as any change may be reflected in the test results. It is also desirable that the same operator carries out the test, for comparative results.

Ideally, all slump results should be 'true' slumps. Unfortunately, this is not the case in practice and three different types of slump may be observed: true, shear and collapse. This is rather a disadvantage since they are not strictly comparable and it is possible to get, say, true and shear slumps from nominally similar mixes. Collapse slumps usually occur with very wet mixes and are probably indicative of rather poor concrete. Shear slumps occur unpredictably but generally in mixes with lower mortar contents; the concrete lacks sufficient binding quality to keep the coarse aggregate integral. Leaner mixes generally are more prone to shear slumps than richer mixes. True slumps are more likely to be obtained consistently with rich mixes.

Mixes of similar numerical values of slump but of different proportions need not exhibit the same workability. For instance, a 6:1 mix with a 50 mm slump will be less workable than a 4·5:1 mix containing the same type of aggregates, also with a 50 mm slump. In general, a richer mix of given slump will be more workable than a leaner mix of the same slump. Another point in connection with slump values and richness of mix concerns the range of test results obtained from nominally identical batches; as the mix gets leaner the range usually increases. A rich mix may have a tolerance of ±5 to 10 mm, whereas a lean mix may have a tolerance of ±25 mm or more. For normal concrete a general guide might be ±25 mm tolerance up to 75 mm slump and plus or minus one-third the value of the slump for slumps greater than 75 mm. Practical limitations might be placed on the values outside of which the test ceases to be of much use and 10 mm to, say, 100 or 125 mm would be reasonable.

The test is most useful, therefore, with richer mixes where the expected slump is between about 10 mm and, say, 100 mm.

Probably the most useful aspect of this test is that one can easily imagine what concrete of a particular slump looks like; a numerical value of slump is a very useful guide for the mind's eye; it is somewhat unfortunate that a test result may sometimes bear little relation to the appearance of the concrete.

2.3.2 The compacting factor test

As a result of the shortcomings of the slump test, particularly with regard to drier concrete, the compacting factor test was developed at the Road Research Laboratory.[3] In developing this test it was realised that the amount of work necessary to achieve full compaction was very difficult to measure accurately so the procedure was changed to measuring the amount of compaction resulting from a fixed amount of work. During the test, work is done on the concrete by allowing it to drop from the hoppers to the cylinder and the weight of concrete thus compacted into the cylinder is divided by the weight of the same volume of fully compacted concrete. This ratio is the compacting factor and is, of course, always less than unity. Workabilities thus measured can vary from about 0·70 to greater than 0·95 corresponding respectively to extremely low workability, requiring intense vibration to compact it, and high workability, suitable for difficult placing and compacting conditions.

The advantages of this test are that it will indicate relative workabilities of mixes which do not slump, within the normal range of cement contents and workabilities (say 250 to 450 kg of cement per cubic metre of compacted concrete and compacting factors 0·80 to 0·95); it distinguishes between the relative workabilities of mixes of different proportions and will usually confirm an experienced visual assessment of the concrete. When used outside the normal range it becomes relatively inaccurate; very rich mixes usually yield values lower than, and very lean mixes values higher than, the actual workability. Mixes of very low compacting factor generally do not adequately reflect, in the test, their true behaviour under vibration; the test is more insensitive to changes in workability above 0·95 compacting factor.

An inherent advantage in doing this test is that the weight of a known volume of compacted concrete is obtained; from this weight the wet density and cement content can be computed. Both of these figures are useful to know and are of practical importance on a site.

2.3.3 The 'V–B' test

This test, Swedish in origin, has been in use for some years in this country, though largely for research purposes. However, in recent times it has become more widespread in use and has been adopted by various members of the concrete industry: ready-mixed concrete suppliers, the precast industry and some civil engineering sites. As usually performed this test measures the time required to change the shape of the concrete from a standard-compacted slump cone to a flat cylinder, under vibration. This time is related not only to the workability of the concrete, but also to the mobility or deformability. In practice, since both of these properties are important and inter-related we lose little in combining them under the heading 'work-ability' and therefore the test may be described as a workability test. (For research purposes it may be necessary and/or desirable to treat them separately.)

Typical times corresponding to different workabilities, as measured by the compacting factor, are:

compacting factor	0·95	0·85	0·75
'V–B' (sec)	2–3	8–12	15–20

Some points to note are that with the high workability concrete the length of the 'V–B' time is so short that a small error in time measurement—½ or 1 sec—is a large proportion of the total time; it would therefore seem that the test is not very suitable for this type of concrete. At the other extreme it sometimes happens that with the drier mixes virtually 100% contact area between transparent plate and concrete is evident after, say, 15 sec, but prolonged vibration is required to finally eliminate perhaps one or two air bubbles on the surface. The recorded time may well be in the region of 30 sec, whereas the workability corresponds to about 15 sec vibration.

This, and the general problem of eliminating operator error in judging the end of the test, has led to the development of an auto-matic recording device which plots the vertical movement, with time, of the transparent plate. A permanent record, independent of the operator, is thus obtained. It is probably of most use in distinguishing between the end-points of very dry or harsh mixes which require long periods of vibration.

Theoretically one needs to adjust the recorded time in this test by the factor V_f/V_c (where V_c = bulk volume of the cone, V_f = final volume in the pot) to allow for work done in effecting this volume change, which is different for concretes of different workabilities. However, unless the workability is very low this can be neglected;[6] it is of no practical significance.

Because this test uses vibration as a means of measuring workability it is realistic in so far as most concrete is vibrated rather than hand-tamped. It can deal with a wide range of mixes—wide in the range of workability and richness—and gives, in general, good reproducibility. The equipment is fairly expensive, but there is a small vibrating table incorporated in it and this is very useful for manufacturing test specimens of various types.

2.4 GENERAL COMMENTS ON MEASURING WORKABILITY

All methods reduce workability to a simple 'engineering' figure: a number of inches with slump, a numerical ratio with compacting factor, time in seconds with 'V–B'. This limits the scope of the tests. The results obtained are specific to each test, *e.g.* Fig. 2.1 shows a typical relationship between 'V–B', slump and compacting factor.[7] It can be seen that for a given 'V–B' time a rich mix will have a lower compacting factor than a lean mix. In other words, the tests are not directly comparable over a range of richness of mix. Figure 2.2 shows, diagrammatically, ranges of workability over which these tests are most useful and Table 2.1 shows typical numerical values of compacting factor and 'V–B' for different levels of workability and for rich and lean concretes. Other properties of the concrete, *e.g.* the finishability and stability characteristics, are not directly indicated by these tests.

Summing up it might be said that the visual judgement of workability and handling characteristics of the concrete are not easily measured.

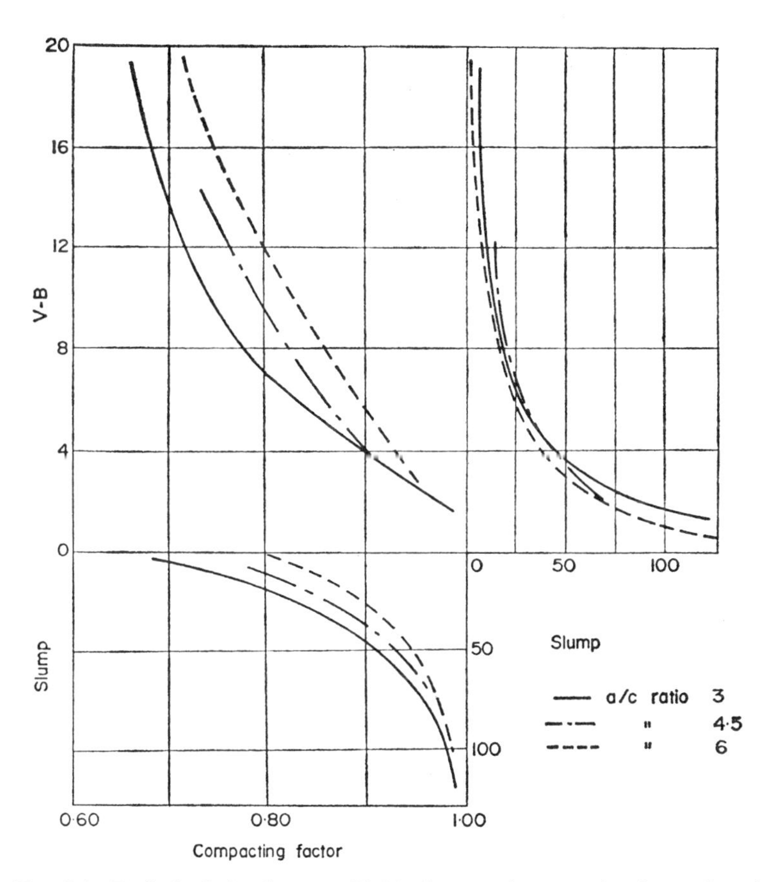

FIG. 2.1 Typical relation between 'V–B', slump and compacting factor (based on Ref. 7).

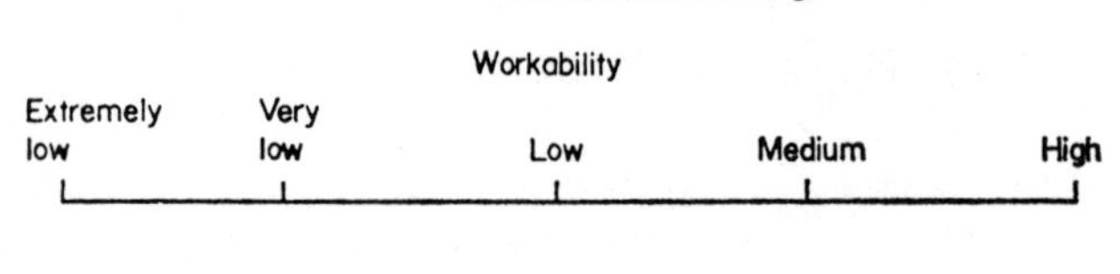

FIG. 2.2 Diagrammatic representation of suitable ranges of workability for 'V–B' slump and compacting factor.

TABLE 2.1
Relation between compacting factor and 'V–B'

Aggregate/cement ratio (by weight)	Compacting factor			
	0·95	0·90	0·85	0·80
	'V–B' (seconds)			
6–9	1–2	4–6	9–12	17–22
3	2–3	3–5	4–6	6–8

2.5 FACTORS AFFECTING WORKABILITY

As already indicated, the property 'workability' is very complex and the role of the various factors influencing it is impossible to state in precise, quantitative terms. The effects of the interaction of these factors change with changing circumstances and rationalising the underlying behaviour is extremely difficult. However, for the concrete technologist concerned with practical effects the following are probably the more important influences:

water content
aggregate properties
cement content

2.5.1 Water content

For given materials and proportions the workability increases with increase in water content per cubic metre of concrete:

Cement content (kg/m^3)	Water content (kg/m^3)	Compacting factor
300	135	0·83
300	150	0·92
300	165	0·96

If the water content is held constant then the richness of the mix can be varied over quite wide limits without causing an appreciable change in the workability. Figure 2.3 is based on data given in Road Note No. 4[(8)] and Research Report No. 2[(9)] and shows the relation between water content (kg/m^3) and compacting factor for graded aggregates of three different maximum sizes and similar sand contents. The data are meant to illustrate typical relations only and were computed for cement contents from about 250 to about 450 kg/m^3.

Although it is very much an over-simplification, it is nevertheless a useful maxim that 'constant water content means constant workability' for given materials.

In practice, therefore, if we know what water content we require to obtain a certain degree of workability—this can be measured in a trial mix—we can use it to obtain a mix of very similar workability but of different cement content (*see* Chapter 4).

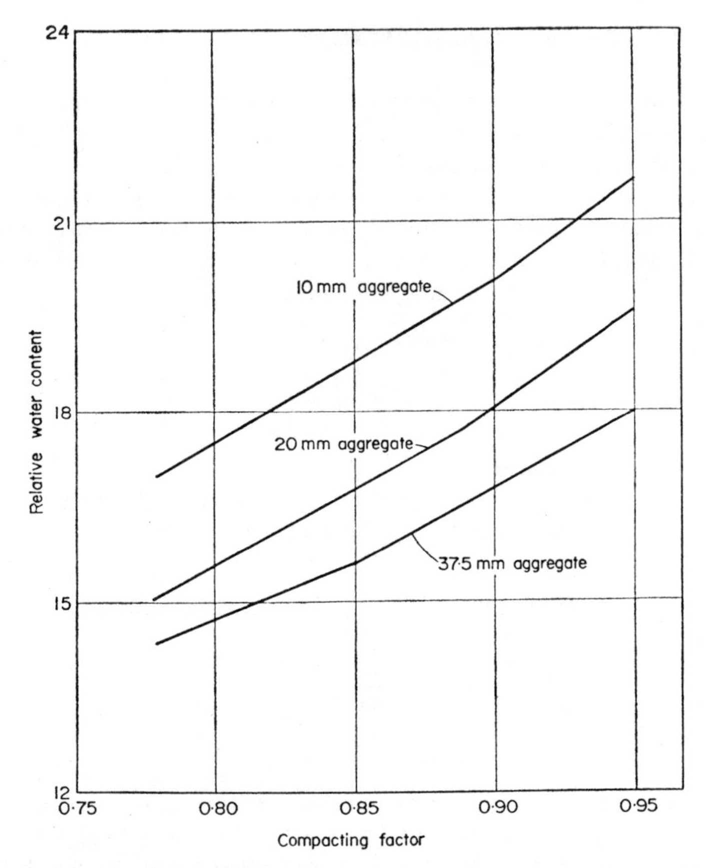

FIG. 2.3 Typical relation between water content, compacting factor and maximum size of aggregate.

2.5.2 Aggregate properties

Some aggregate properties which affect workability are maximum particle size, particle shape and surface texture, and grading or particle size distribution.

(i) Maximum particle size

From Fig. 2.3 we find that to produce concretes of comparable strengths and similar workabilities—with, say, a compacting factor of about 0·85—using aggregates of similar particle shape but of different maximum size, we need mixes as shown below if each is to have a water/cement ratio of, say, 0·50:

Maximum aggregate size (mm)	Approximate water content (kg/m³)	Cement content to obtain strength (kg/m³)	Corresponding aggregate/ cement ratio
37·5	155	310	6·0
20·0	169	338	5·5
10·0	189	378	4·5

As the aggregate size decreases we have to add more water to maintain workability; if we assume that, to obtain the required strength, with 37·5 mm aggregate, we need 310 kg of cement per cubic metre of concrete, then as we increase the water content with 20·0 mm aggregate we must proportionally increase the cement content. Likewise with the 10·0 mm aggregate. Therefore, on the grounds of economy in cost of materials, one should use the largest size aggregate, compatible with the conditions imposed by the structure. In general, in main structural members where the cover to the reinforcement is small and the distance between bars is also small, 20·0 mm maximum size aggregate will probably be best, and, occasionally, 10·0 mm may have to be used. In bases and floors, 37·5 mm may be acceptable, but most contractors will probably use the one size throughout rather than have an extra stockpile and different mixes. Where ready-mixed concrete is used there is no site storage problem.

(*ii*) *Particle shape and surface texture*

Although common sense tells us that the surface roughness of aggregate must influence workability it is not clear what the value of this influence is and at least one research worker[10] has found no statistical relation between widely varied textures and compacting factor.

The effect of particle shape, on the other hand, has been evaluated in various ways. The simplest is that based on the BS 812[11] subjective assessment: rounded, irregular, angular. The data below show the effect of a change of overall particle shape, *i.e. in fine and coarse aggregate*, on the aggregate/cement ratio for low workability concrete with a water/cement ratio of 0·50 using 20·0 mm maximum size aggregate:

Aggregate particle shape	Aggregate/cement ratio by weight
Rounded	7·5
Irregular	5·5
Angular	4·7

If, instead of having the fine and coarse aggregates of the same particle shape we use a fine aggregate of irregular shape with coarse aggregates of rounded, irregular and angular particles, we find the following:

Aggregate particle size	Aggregate/cement ratio by weight
Rounded coarse and irregular fine	6·5
Irregular coarse and irregular fine	5·5
Angular coarse and irregular fine	5·2

The effect of changing the coarse aggregate shape but maintaining constant fine aggregate shape is not as great as one might imagine: in the above table the difference between an (irregular coarse) + (irregular fine) and (angular coarse) + (irregular fine) aggregate is fairly small—5·5 to 5·2 aggregate/cement ratio—and, though these figures are very approximate, they give the right order of difference. With (rounded coarse) + (rounded fine) and (rounded coarse) + (irregular fine) the difference would be greater—7·5 to 6·5—because there is a greater difference in particle shape between rounded and irregular than between irregular and angular—(rounded coarse) + (rounded fine) compared with, say, (irregular coarse) + (rounded fine) would probably yield aggregate/cement ratios of 7·5 and about 7·2 respectively. In other words, the particle shape of the fine aggregate has more influence on workability than that of the coarse aggregate.

The previous paragraph is, of necessity, rather vague since the definition of particle shape was qualitative rather than quantitative. With the development of the angularity number test[12] and its incorporation in BS 812[11] an objective, quantitative measure has become available. It has been possible to correlate particle shape, defined by angularity number, and workability, defined by compacting factor,[10] and Murdock[13] has suggested a method of predicting the compacting factor knowing the shape and grading of the aggregates (*see* Chapter 5).

(*iii*) *Aggregate grading*
Grading refers not only to the percentage of sand, but also to the overall range of particle sizes passing the various sieves. Assuming that the grading is synonymous with sand content can be very misleading, *e.g.* a mix with 35% of a Zone 1 sand will be distinctly different from one with 35% Zone 4 sand. If we fix the sand grading as, say, Zone 2,[14] then for convenience we can think of overall gradings in terms of sand content. In general, the sand content of a concrete for a Zone 2 sand may vary from about 30% to about 50% of the total aggregate, the actual amount depending upon numerous factors such as workability, richness, shape of aggregate, shape of section to be cast, and so on. There is no 'ideal' sand content which is universally applicable; the amount will vary depending upon the relative influence of the factors mentioned previously. We can, however, generalise and say that an increase in sand content, at the low end of the workability range, may cause a more noticeable drop in workability than at the higher end of the range where greater sand contents are necessary and an increase has not such a measurable effect. There are two extremes to avoid, under-sanding and over-sanding, but, on balance, it is better to have a tendency towards the latter than the former. If a mix is poised on the brink of the optimum sand content—on the grounds of workability—it requires only a batching error to result in a poor mix. With some sand in hand, so to speak, there is some latitude permissible. Higher sand contents are desirable for leaner mixes, coarser sands, higher workabilities, poorer aggregate shape, smaller size of aggregate, more awkwardly shaped sections and more congested sections.

(*iv*) *Concept of specific surface*
The specific surface is defined as the ratio of surface area to volume and is normally expressed as m^2/m^3. Because of the difficulty of measuring volume and because the volume is related to weight through the specific gravity, it is common practice to express the

ratio as surface area to weight (m^2/g). Consider a cube of side 1 mm and weighing 1 g:

the surface area = $6 \times 1\ mm^2 = 6 \times 10^{-6}\ m^2$
the weight = 1 g
therefore, the specific surface = $6 \times 10^{-6}\ m^2/g$

Consider another cube which has a side equal to twice that of the first cube, *i.e.* 2 mm, and is of the same density:

its surface area = $6 \times 4\ mm^2 = 24 \times 10^{-6}\ m^2$
its weight = 8 g
its specific surface = $24/8 = 3 \times 10^{-6}\ m^2/g$
i.e. half that of the smaller cube

Now, as the specific surface increases it means that for a given weight more surface area is exposed. (In our example, for 1 g we have $6 \times 10^{-6}\ m^2$ and $3 \times 10^{-6}\ m^2$ of area exposed for the two cubes.) The more surface area exposed the more water and cement paste will be required to wet that area and therefore the less will be left for lubrication of the mix and thus the lower will be the workability. Applying this reasoning to concrete aggregates, and assuming that the shape does not change as the particle size decreases, the specific surface of the 37·5 mm size would be about half that of the 20·0 mm size and about one-quarter that of the 10·0 mm size. So a decrease in maximum size would increase the specific surface and therefore the 'water demand' for a constant workability. Likewise, a finer grading would have a higher specific surface than a coarser grading so that increasing the sand content or using the same weight of a finer sand would increase the 'water demand'. The aggregate shape with the lowest specific is, ideally, spherical so that the rounder the aggregate the better the workability; the more it deviates from this the lower the workability.

This concept of specific surface is only partly true but it is useful as a general principle, particularly as far as aggregate gradings are concerned (*see* Chapter 5). Figure 2.4 illustrates qualitatively a relation between workability and grading that is perhaps more realistic and is fairly typical of what is observed in practice.

2.5.3 Cement content

For normal mixes, *i.e.* where the cement content is not too high (say less than 380 kg/m^3) this effect is negligible and may be ignored. But as mixes get very rich the amount of cement influences the compacting factor such that an apparent drop occurs. It is also found that in very rich mixes (say richer than about 450 kg of cement per cubic metre of concrete) the fineness of the cement affects workability, a finer cement resulting in an apparent drop in compacting factor (*see* Chapter 7).

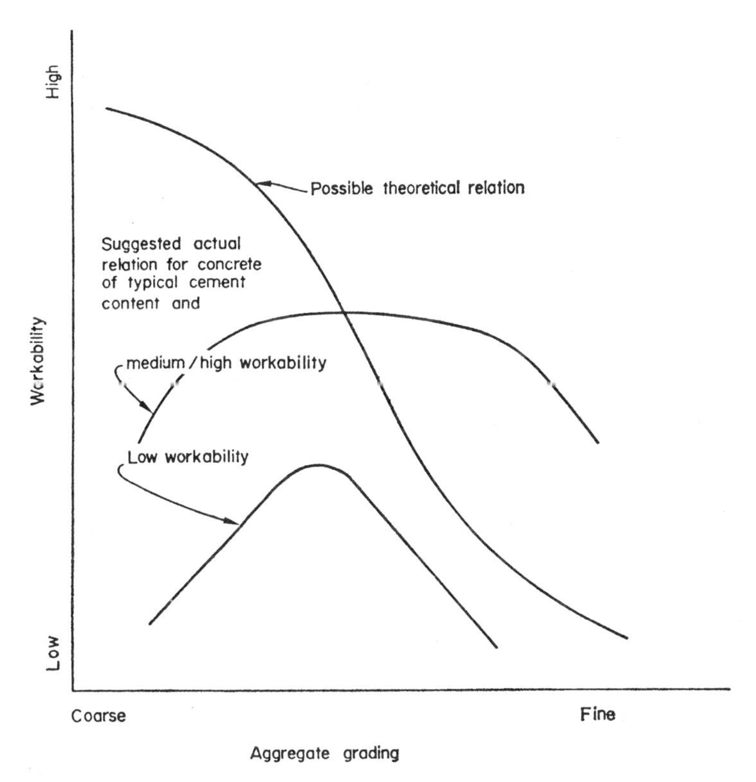

FIG. 2.4 Qualitative relation between workability and aggregate grading.

2.6 LEVELS OF WORKABILITY SUITABLE FOR CONCRETE FOR DIFFERENT USES

This is a most important step in selecting our mix proportions. Table 4.2 (p. 44) suggests values of slump, compacting factor and 'V–B' for different degrees of workability.

2.7 THE STABILITY OF PLASTIC CONCRETE

Plastic concrete should be such that it remains as homogeneous as possible from mixing to final compaction. With a correctly proportioned mix this is no problem, but, where the mortar consistence and/or quantity is incorrect, segregation will occur making it very difficult or impossible to produce compacted concrete with the required properties.

In most cases (*see* Chapter 6 for an exception) the amount and consistence of the mortar should be sufficient to hold the coarse aggregate particles together. Lack of mortar, or too high or too low a consistence, will induce lack of cohesiveness; the mix will not 'hang together' very well and movement, such as transporting and placing operations, will separate the mortar component from the aggregate. Assume that we have a mix that is stable enough; keeping the ratios cement/fine aggregate/coarse aggregate constant but using mixes with successively lower water contents we reach the stage where the coarse aggregate will separate from the mix because the mortar is too dry. This is dry segregation. It is, of course, most uncommon on construction sites.

Wet segregation, which occurs much more frequently, is due to adding more and more water to our stable mix. We reduce the cohesiveness of the mortar until it separates out from the mix, leaving the coarse aggregate. The problem of wet segregation may be treated thus:

(a) reduce the water content of the mix;
(b) add more sand;
(c) add the same weight, but of a finer sand, as that already in the mix;
(d) add more cement;
(e) use a smaller maximum size aggregate.

When the mix is too wet either reducing the amount of water or that in conjunction with (b), (c), (d) or (e) should make it sufficiently stable. If the segregation is very bad then obviously the entire mix proportions need reviewing.

There will be times when extra stability is demanded from a mix because of, for example, transporting or placing methods and then extra care must be taken to ensure that there is sufficient cohesive mortar present to maintain homogeneity. This is discussed in Chapter 4. Since, in general, it is quite easy to produce a stable concrete mix (and corrective action, where required, is simple) there is really no excuse for instability and, apart from the very minor intrinsic lack of stability in all concretes, arising out of the composition used, there should be no practical difficulties.

Chapter 3

THE PROPERTIES OF HARDENED CONCRETE

3.1 WHY STRENGTH?

There are, of course, many properties that are of importance in hardened concrete, *e.g.* strength, durability, density, permeability, dimensional stability, appearance, and so on. At times some of these are of prime importance while others are secondary in desirability. The anchorage zones in prestressed concrete members obviously need high strength concrete; lack of strength would be serious, if not catastrophic. Concrete subjected to severe weathering or exposed to a corrosive atmosphere will require durability primarily; it may have good structural strength but that may be quite incidental. Water retaining structures should be permeable to a minimum degree, though they will generally have considerable strength as well.

There are many such examples. However, frequently it is difficult or impossible to measure some of these properties: density is notoriously difficult; durability is impossible except on a long-term basis; appearance is subjective; dimensional stability is difficult and long-term; permeability is difficult; and so on with many properties. Now strength, or some measure of it, is relatively easy to evaluate and as it is roughly indicative of the quality of concrete in other directions—as strength increases, density, permeability, durability, etc., generally improve—it has been accepted as a general index to the overall concrete quality, despite the fact that it may often be of secondary importance.

The strength itself may be classified into compressive, tensile and bond strengths. Here again, some may take priority over others but because of difficulties associated with tensile and bond tests and because these are properties roughly related to compressive strength we have accepted the latter as a measure of general strength of the concrete. Methods of measuring certain aspects of tensile strength are now common and these will be discussed later.

3.2 COMPRESSIVE STRENGTH

The compressive strength of concrete is empirically a function of the following:

water/cement ratio
compaction
cement type
aggregate type
aggregate/cement ratio
specimen type and geometry
testing procedure
age } maturity
curing }

3.2.1 Water/cement ratio

If concrete is fully compacted the compressive strength for a given set of materials at a given age is inversely proportional to the ratio of the weight of water in the concrete to the weight of cement:

$$\left[\mu = \varphi\left(\frac{1}{w/c}\right)\right]$$

where μ = compressive strength, w = weight of water, c = weight of cement and φ = a constant dependent upon materials, age and testing conditions.

A typical relation between compressive strength and water/cement ratio is shown in Fig. 3.1. According to this a 7:1 mix with a water/cement ratio 0·55 would have the same strength as a 4:1 mix with a water/cement ratio of 0·55, at the same age and containing similar materials. This is a very convenient relation, but it is not entirely true; for normal workabilities and strength it is, however quite reasonable.

We say that

$$\left[\mu = \varphi\left(\frac{1}{w/c}\right)\right]$$

i.e.

$$\left[\mu = \varphi\left(\frac{c}{w}\right)\right]$$

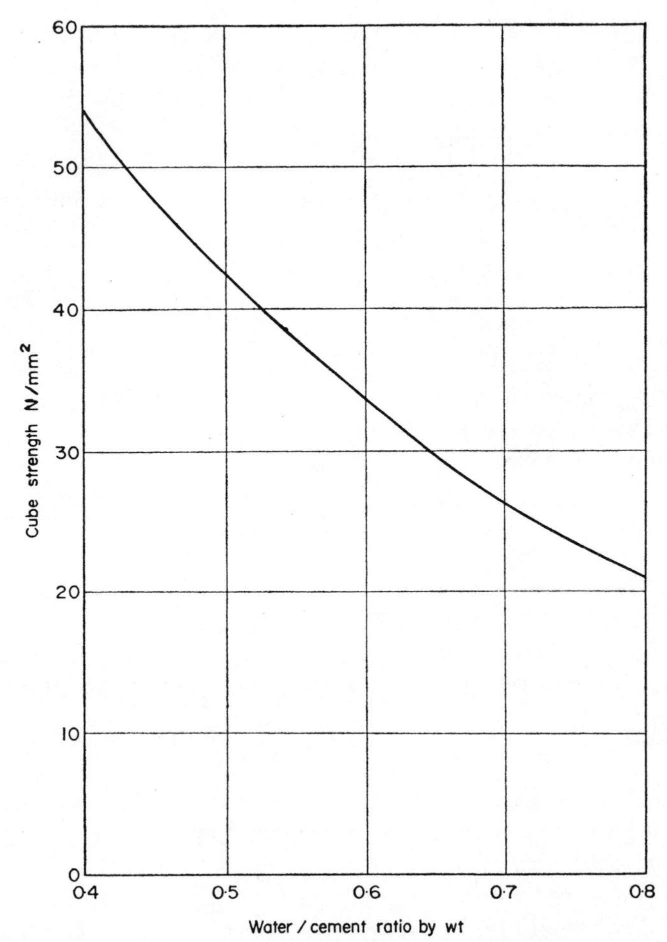

FIG. 3.1 Typical relation between cube strength and water/cement ratio.

Figure 3.2 shows this and it will be noted that it is sensibly a straight line relation. This is therefore a much more convenient way of dealing with it than the former one since to establish the relation for a particular cement one needs only two or three points to fix the slope of the line. However, although various people have for many years advocated the use of cement/water instead of water/cement ratio we still adhere to the latter in the UK.

The weight of water in the mix needs to be defined since there are two extremes that can be adopted. We can take the total weight of water in the mix; this is equal to the water added at the mixer plus the total water in the aggregates. The latter consists of water inside the particles, filling the aggregate pores, plus 'free' water trapped on the surfaces of and between the aggregate particles.

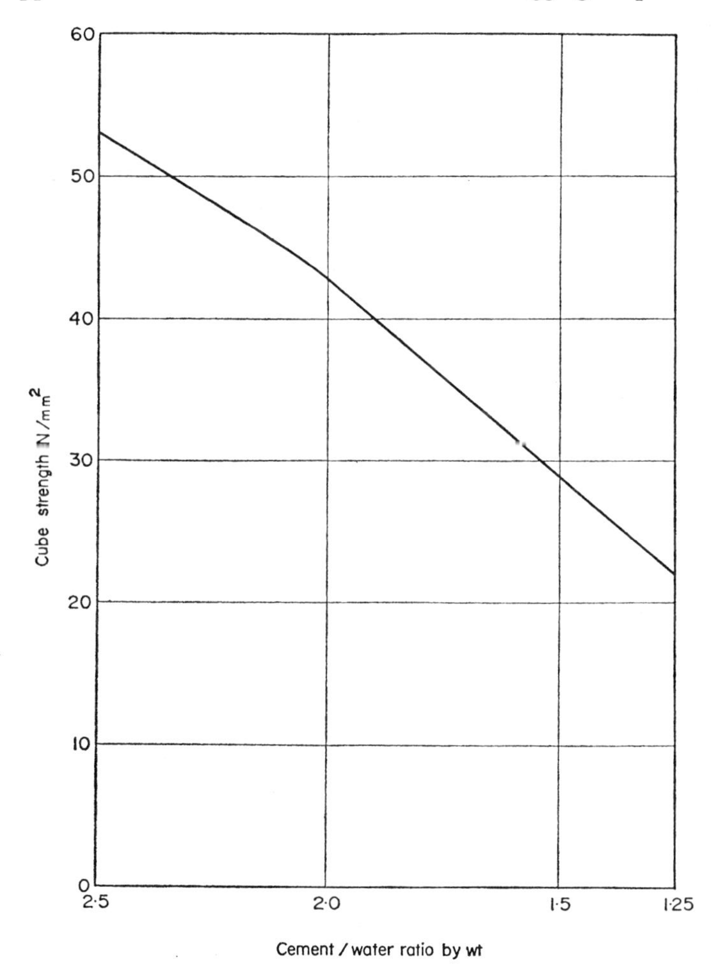

FIG. 3.2 Typical relation between cube strength and cement/water ratio.

Thus, if a sample of sand, from an aggregate stockpile, was oven-dried and showed a total moisture content of 6%, this would be about 1% moisture actually inside the sand particle and 5% outside on the surfaces of the particles. Our 'total water'/cement ratio would include this 1% moisture (and whatever was inside the coarse aggregates, usually 1 to 2%).

The 'free water'/cement ratio excludes the latter and takes account only of water on the surfaces of and between aggregate particles plus that added at the mixer, *i.e.* water that is readily accessible to reaction with the cement. Because of difficulties associated with this procedure—notably the exact determination of water inside the aggregate pores—laboratory practice has frequently been to use dry aggregates and 'total water'/cement ratios. Some mix design data therefore refer to 'total' rather than 'free' water. The strength and workability versus water/cement ratio relations are therefore dependent upon the definition of water/cement ratio. In general, 'free water'/cement ratio is preferred here unless otherwise stated.

3.2.2 Compaction

The original relation propounded by Feret was of the form

$$\left[\mu = \psi\left(\frac{1}{(w + v)/c}\right)\right]$$

where μ = compressive strength, w = volume of water voids, v = volume of air voids, c = volume of cement and ψ = empirical constant.

If the concrete is fully compacted then $v = 0$ and we get the strength water/cement ratio relation of Section 3.2.1.

The effect of air voids, owing to under compaction, is difficult to evaluate but is usually taken as shown in Fig. 3.3. This is based on Road Research Laboratory Technical Paper No. 5.[3] It can be taken that for every 1% under-compaction there is a 5 to 6% loss in compressive strength. If, then, some fully compacted cubes yielded a strength of 35 N/mm^2 at 7 days, with 95% compaction (5% under-compaction) there would be a loss of 25 to 30%, *i.e.* 9 to 11 N/mm^2. The strength would thus be 24 to 26 N/mm^2.

It is exceedingly difficult to get full compaction, even in the laboratory; there is usually about 1% air left in the concrete. How much more likely is it, therefore, that site-compacted concrete is not fully compacted? Hence the importance of workability in making it as easy as is economically possible to achieve compaction on site.

Figure 3.4 shows the results of decreasing the water/cement ratio for a fixed aggregate/cement ratio. Increased strength is obtained as long as effective compactive efforts are used. When the workability is very low the lack of compaction (in this case due to hand tamping) is serious enough to cause a large drop in strength. It will be obvious that this is most important, not only as far as the concrete structure is concerned, but also as far as concrete cubes are concerned. They must

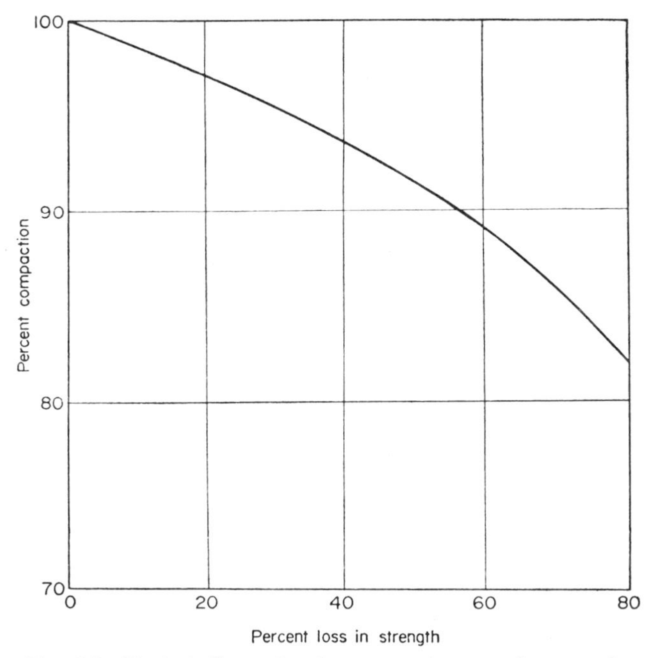

FIG. 3.3 Typical effects of under-compaction on cube strength.

be fully compacted (to eliminate that source of variation). BS 1881[15] does not ask for 25 blows of the standard hand-punner per 50 mm layer of concrete in 100 mm cubes, and 35 blows per layer for the 150 mm cube. It asks for a *minimum* number of blows, which with a workable concrete will be at least 25 to 35 respectively. The spirit of BS 1881 requires *full* compaction.

3.2.3 Cement type

The type of cement affects the rate of hydration, so that strengths at early ages can be considerably influenced by the particular cement used, whereas strengths after, say, twelve months are hardly affected. For practical purposes it is reasonable to assume that all

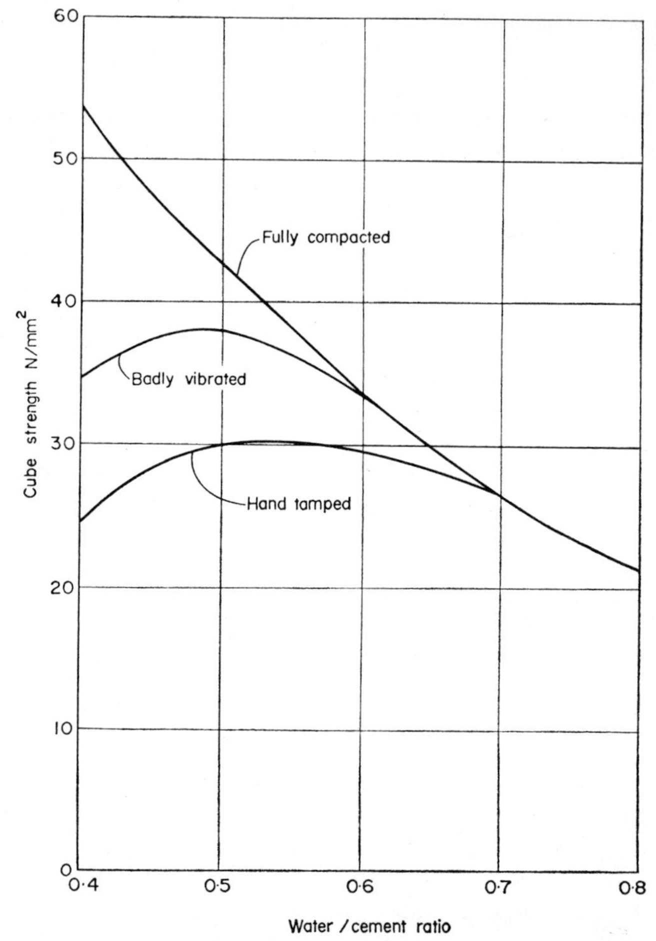

FIG. 3.4 Typical relation between strength, water/cement ratio and compaction.

Portland cements will result in about the same strength (for comparable mixes) at twelve months.

An average, ordinary Portland cement will give a concrete with about 80 to 85% of the strength obtained with an average, rapid hardening Portland cement, of the same mix proportions, at 7 days. At 28 days it may be about 90%.

Portland blastfurnace cement will in general result in strengths similar to those obtained with ordinary Portland cement at 28 days. At early ages it may be lower.

Sulphate resisting Portland cement and white cement will usually be similar to ordinary Portland cement in strength development.

If coloured cements are used, where the colour is obtained by adding inert pigment to the Portland cement, 10 to 15% extra cement should be allowed for to counteract this. For other cements *e.g.* high alumina, supersulphated and extra-rapid hardening Portland cements, reference should be made to the appropriate literature.[16,17]

3.2.4 Aggregate type

For normal strength concrete, *i.e.* where the strength in question does not exceed about 35 to 40 N/mm^2 (at any age), there is little difference between various good quality, natural aggregates (for lightweight aggregates, *see* Chapter 9). Poor quality, natural aggregates may reduce the strength considerably, but good granites, limestones, quartzites, flints, and so on will produce concretes of similar compressive strength for similar water/cement ratios.

Where compressive strengths greater than about 50 to 55 N/mm^2 are required the aggregate type may play a very significant part. In general a sound crushed rock will give a higher strength than a sound gravel for comparable mixes. This is discussed in Chapter 7 on high strength concrete.

3.2.5 Aggregate/cement ratio

For a given water/cement ratio the higher the aggregate/cement ratio the higher the compressive strength tends to be, for mixes of the same aggregate type, *i.e.* a leaner mix will give a higher strength than a rich mix. Practical limitations owing to the means of compaction available curb the benefits obtainable from this. The effect is very pronounced with very low workability, higher strength concretes (*see* Chapter 7).

3.2.6 Specimen type and geometry

Cubes are the standard type of test specimen in the UK and 150 mm cubes are the standard size. Where the aggregate being used does not exceed 25 mm maximum size it is permissible to use 100 mm cubes. For practical purposes it is advantageous to use the latter; they weigh only about 2·5 kg as against 8·5 to 9·0 kg for the former; they take about 0·001 m^3 of concrete (and space in storage) as compared with about 0·003 m^3; they require less than half the load required by 150 mm cubes to cause the same compressive stress (30 N/mm^2 in a 100 mm cube requires a force of 300 kN; a 150 mm cube requires 675 kN); they therefore require a test machine of less than half the load capacity; they take less time to compact; and the moulds must be considerably cheaper than 150 mm cube moulds.

Objections are sometimes raised to the use of 100 mm cubes on the grounds of increased strengths obtained with them. Without delving into the apparent effect of cube size—which is by no means clear cut—whatever the effect is it is irrelevant since the test does not measure a fundamental property of the concrete, but is a control test only.

The cubical shape influences the result in so far as the end restraints—between contact surfaces of concrete and steel platen—cause an apparent increase in compressive strength. By lengthening the specimen while keeping its width constant, *i.e.* increasing the height/width ratio, the effects of end restraint are minimised over the portion of the specimen away from the test machine platens and this results in an apparent decrease in strength. Therefore cylinders with a height/diameter ratio between one and two will exhibit strengths lower than cubes from the same mix. BS 1881(18) shows a figure relating length/diameter ratios of cores to correction factors, which are used to correct the strength of a non-standard core to that of an equivalent standard core with a length/diameter ratio of two. The latter value is then multiplied by 1·25 to give an estimate of the cube strength.

3.2.7 Testing procedure

Considerable evidence has been documented in recent years regarding the effects of testing procedure on the apparent cube strength. It is now firmly established that large changes can be caused by merely changing the testing machine and that factors such as stressing rate, moisture condition of test specimen and lack of care in the placing of the cube in the machine can result in significant departures from the expected strength.

For control purposes (and particularly for checking for compliance with specification requirements) it is vital that the correct test procedure should be followed(18) and that testing machines should be calibrated, preferably against a machine of known, acceptable behaviour.

3.2.8 Age

Unless some inhibiting factor is present, such as lack of curing, concrete gains strength with time until the limiting strength is reached. This limiting strength will be imposed by one of the following: the paste strength, the aggregate strength or the aggregate/paste bond. Figure 3.5 illustrates typical age/strength curves for low strength, medium strength and high strength concrete with ordinary Portland cement.

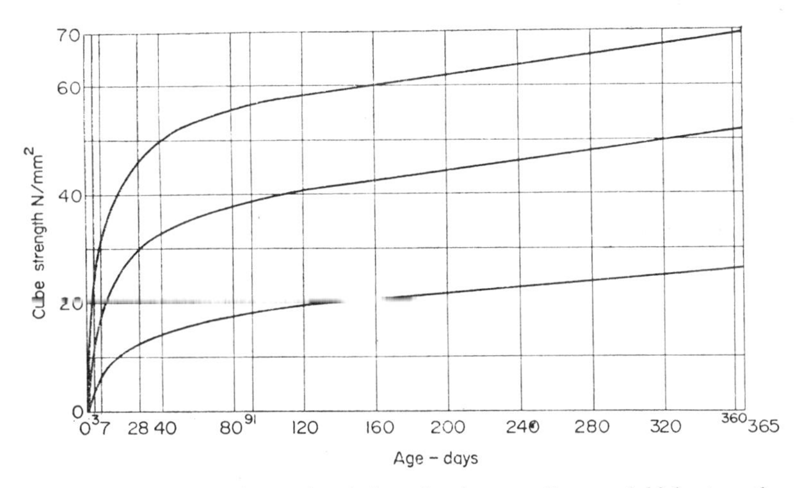

FIG. 3.5 Typical age/strength relations for low, medium and high strength concrete with ordinary Portland cement.

3.2.9 Curing

Since the strength of concrete depends considerably upon the hydration of the cement, it is essential that moisture is present to enable hydration to continue. This is provided by the curing process. At the same time, hydration is affected by temperature, a high temperature accelerating it and a low temperature retarding it. Therefore, provided concrete is not allowed to dry out but is cured by maintaining it in a wet condition, its strength would appear to be a function of time (its age) and temperature. This time and temperature concept implies that the concrete strength would be the same whether it was cured for a short period of time at higher temperatures or for a longer period of time at lower temperatures. The product of temperature and time is called maturity.

In principle this concept seems logical but in practice it becomes very difficult to establish an accurate relationship which covers all temperature–time regimes. For further information on this matter the reader is referred to *Magazine of Concrete Research* Nos. 22[19] and 24[20] and to the 1954 Symposium on Mix Design and Quality Control.[21]

The standard curing temperatures for test specimens are 20 ± 1°C for laboratory curing and for site curing 20 ± 5°C for the first 16 to 24 h and 20 ± 2°C thereafter.[15]

3.3 TENSILE STRENGTH

Direct tensile testing of concrete is very difficult and so other tests have been developed which are easier to perform but which are indirect in their approach. The oldest and most established of these is the modulus of rupture test which is a measure of the bending tensile strength. Two forms of this test have been used; one method required beams to be tested under centre-point loading and the other under third-point loading, the spans also being different. Different results were obtained from each method.

The latter is the BS 1881 method which, although it gives lower results, is more reliable as a test and is therefore preferred. It is very important that the specimens are kept wet until they are tested as even slight drying out introduces shrinkage stresses in the outer skin, where, of course, the highest bending stresses occur, thus causing premature failure.

The modulus of rupture is typically related to compressive strength as shown in Fig. 3.6. The former is tending towards a limiting strength, imposed by the inherent strength of the concrete, as the latter increases. This relationship is of the form

$$[fb = \mathrm{a}\mu^{\mathrm{b}}]$$

where fb = modulus of rupture (N/mm^2), μ = compressive strength (N/mm^2) and a, b = constants whose values depend upon the size of beam, the method of test and the type of aggregate.

These beam specimens are often further tested after the bending strength has been determined; each end is then tested as an 'equivalent' cube, as laid down in BS 1881,[18] and a measure of the compressive strength obtained. This may not be the same as that of a normal cube from the same batch of concrete, owing to the different specimen shape and to its having been tested previously, but it is indicative of the level of compressive strength and is a useful check.

The modulus of rupture is influenced by the same factors as is the cube strength, though not always to the same degree. Data for mix design are given in Chapter 10.

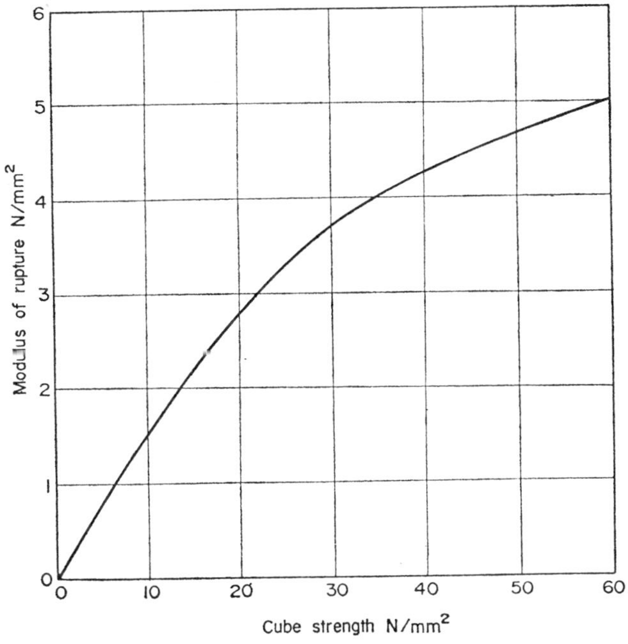

FIG. 3.6 Typical relation between modulus of rupture and cube strength.

3.4 CYLINDER SPLITTING TEST

This is another measure of tensile strength that has become prominent in recent years. A cylinder is compressed across a diameter inducing tensile stresses at right angles to it and causing splitting along it. Details are given in BS 1881. Loading is applied through packing strips and the tensile stress induced is calculated from the expression

$$\left[f_t = \frac{2P}{\pi d l}\right]$$

where f_t = tensile stress (N/mm^2), P = failing load (N), d = diameter of cylinder (mm) and l = length of cylinder (mm).

Advantages claimed for this test are that it can be carried out in the normal cube testing machine and the tensile stresses are, theoretically, induced uniformly over about three-quarters the diameter of the specimen. The strength thus obtained is about two-thirds of the modulus of rupture or one-fifteenth of the compressive strength. It seems to be closely related to the direct tensile strength(22) and is affected largely by the same factors as is the bending strength. Data for mix design are given in Chapter 10.

3.5 THE MODULUS OF ELASTICITY

This is of importance in calculating deflection of beams, loss of stress in prestressed concrete owing to elastic movement, recoverable movement under load, conversion of strain to stress, and so on.

It depends on factors such as:

age of concrete
water/cement ratio
aggregate/cement ratio
type of aggregate
method of test

The first two virtually control strength between them and the modulus of elasticity can be said to depend largely upon the strength of the concrete. This is not entirely correct but for most purposes it is a useful approximation. For most normal aggregates the higher the aggregate/cement ratio the higher will be the modulus of elasticity for a given compressive strength. Aggregate type can have a very serious effect; for instance, lightweight aggregates can produce concrete with an elastic modulus equal to about one-half or two-thirds that of normal concrete of the same strength (*see* Chapter 9). The method of test is such that the static method—where load/deformation measurements are taken over a fairly short period of time—results in a lower modulus of elasticity than the dynamic method—which is a vibrationary technique inducing negligible stresses into the specimen—the relative values of static to dynamic being about 60 to 80% for compressive strengths of about 20 to 45 N/mm^2.

The approximate relation between compressive strength and static modulus for normal aggregate concretes can be taken as below, bearing in mind that considerable variation can occur and large departures from these data can be found:

μ (N/mm^2)	E (kN/mm^2)
20	20
30	25
40	30
50	35
60	38
70	40

μ = cube strength.
E = elastic modulus.

Mixes are not designed on the basis of modulus of elasticity and where knowledge of the latter is important experimental determination is necessary using the desired materials and proportions.

3.6 SHRINKAGE AND CREEP

The movements of concrete due to shrinkage and creep are extremely difficult to predict with accuracy and it is not proposed to deal with them here. Leaner mixes, of low water content, made with stable aggregates will normally exhibit lower shrinkage than rich, wet mixes or those incorporating unstable aggregates. Creep can be taken as being proportional to applied stress, within the normal, permissible working stresses, and therefore as long as the concrete is sufficiently strong creep is no great problem. The ramifications of creep and shrinkage should normally be examined in the context of structural design and, although time-dependent deformation has generally been examined more critically in recent years, especially with the greater usage of more highly stressed, more slender elements, difficulties seldom arise where good concrete technology is practised. Provided that concrete of reasonable strength is chosen, based on sound ingredients, considerations such as amount and disposition of reinforcement, span/depth ratio, degrees of restraint and environmental conditions become dominant.

Where more precise and detailed knowledge is required it is necessary to examine each concrete under relevant conditions.

Chapter 4

THE ROAD NOTE NO. 4 METHOD OF MIX DESIGN

4.1 BASIC APPROACH

The tradititional British method of deriving mix proportions is that outlined in Road Note No. 4.[8] It can be summarised thus:

(a) To satisfy a specified compressive strength and durability, a value of water/cement ratio is chosen, from data given, for the appropriate age and type of Portland cement.
(b) The level of workability of the concrete required is chosen.
(c) Tables are provided relating aggregate/cement ratio, workability and water/cement ratio for aggregates of different particle shape and maximum particle size. Therefore, knowing the available aggregates and having fixed the workability and water/cement ratio, the aggregate/cement ratio can be selected.
(d) The ratio of fine to coarse aggregate is chosen to produce a satisfactory plastic concrete.

It is useful to think of the process, in essence, as follows:

strength and durability → water/cement ratio
workability → water content

$$\frac{\text{water/cement ratio}}{\text{water content}} \rightarrow \text{cement content}$$

cement content → aggregate/cement ratio

and, while this is naturally a simplification of what is involved, it is very helpful because it allows one to assess quickly the likely effects of changes in the controlling parameters. Some examples given later (*see* Section 4.8) will demonstrate this.

Although the principles of Road Note No. 4 are followed here some modifications are introduced which it is hoped should aid the process without serious loss of usefulness. Wherever possible, data are rounded off and simplified and the inherent lack of precision should at all times be borne in mind.

4.2 THE CONCRETE PROPERTIES REQUIRED

The properties of concrete with which we are concerned here are compressive strength, durability, workability and stability. (In achieving a good 'as struck' finish to the concrete the latter two are necessary, so we might say that we are indirectly including appearance as a further property.)

4.2.1 Compressive strength

We assume here that for fully compacted concrete the compressive strength is dependent only upon the water/cement ratio for a given type of cement, age, method of testing and curing. Figure 4.1 shows a relation between compressive strength and water/cement ratio for ordinary Portland cement and for different ages. This figure, which is based on data in Road Note No. 4, gives sufficient material to cover the field of 'normal', as opposed to 'high-strength', structural concrete. It shows the relation in principle, rather than in fact, since the strengths may differ with cements from different sources and with different aggregates.

The figure may be used as follows. If a compressive strength of 27·5 N/mm^2 at 7 days is required, from Fig. 4.1 this corresponds to a nominal free water/cement ratio of about 0·56. It may be found that cubes from the mix, having been made, cured and tested in the standard manner, may consistently have a compressive strength of 34·5 N/mm^2 at 7 days. We then plot this strength on the figure corresponding to a water/cement ratio of 0·56 and mark it 'A'. A new curve may then be drawn, through 'A', following the shape of the nearest curve to it. This can be used to fix the water/cement ratios of subsequent mixes with the same materials and similar workability. Thus, if a strength of 31 N/mm^2 at 7 days were required our new curve would indicate a water/cement ratio of about 0·60; for 24 N/mm^2 it would be about 0·70.

4.2.2 Specified characteristic strength and design mean strength

Let us suppose that we have been asked to produce concrete with a specified characteristic strength of 30 N/mm^2 at 28 days. Being

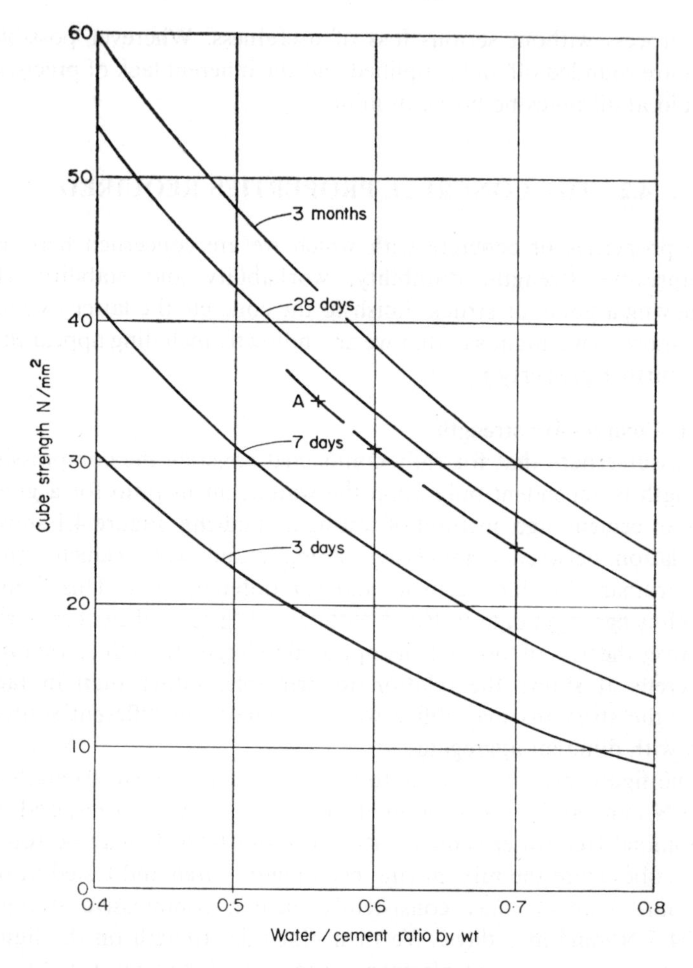

FIG. 4.1 Typical relation between cube strength and water/cement ratio for different ages using ordinary Portland cement.

very cost-conscious we decide that we will not be wasteful through using a mix richer than necessary, but will design a mix aiming for 30 N/mm^2, no more and no less. We argue that to get strengths higher than this is wasteful since we are not asked to do so, while to produce lower strengths is failing to meet the specification. We select our mix proportions, finalise them to get the correct workability and strength on site and start producing concrete.

Cubes are taken and crushed and we plot a record of the results as in Fig. 4.2. It is obvious that, although our *mean* strength is about 30 N/mm^2 (half the results being greater and half less than this), the situation is most unsatisfactory because half the cubes

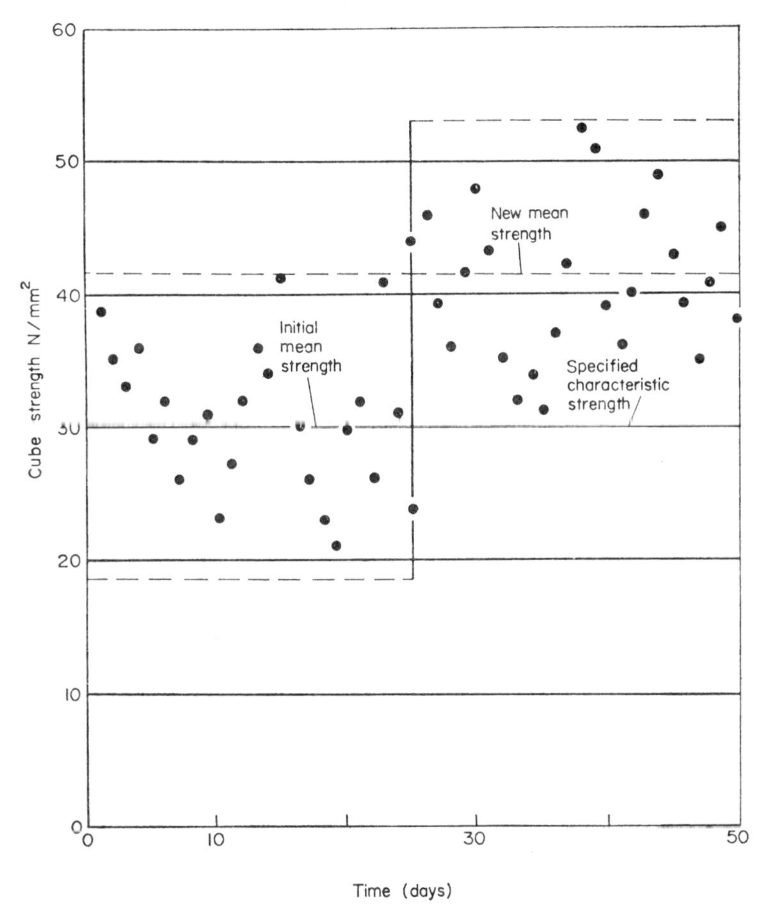

FIG. 4.2 Design mean strength and specified characteristic strength for a given degree of control.

are below the specified characteristic strength. What we have to do, in this case, is to redesign the mix aiming for a higher strength, 41·5 N/mm^2; we then find that, if our control remains unchanged, our mean strength becomes 41·5 N/mm^2 and only a few cubes fall below 30 N/mm^2. We are therefore satisfying the specified characteristic strength.

The relation between the mean and characteristic strengths is a very complex one but it is evidently dependent upon the quality control exercised over the production of the concrete. If such a thing as perfect control existed, no variation in cube strengths would occur and one would aim for a strength equal to the characteristic strength. As the control deteriorates the variation increases and the spread of the cube results gets wider. For poor control this could well cover a range of, say, 30 N/mm^2. The design mean strength would then have to be fixed at about (30/2) N/mm^2 or 15 N/mm^2 above the specified characteristic strength.

A simple example will show the effect of control on the design mean strength and mix proportions:

	Very good control	Poor control
Specified characteristic strength	20 N/mm^2	20 N/mm^2
Design mean strength	29 N/mm^2	37 N/mm^2
Water/cement ratio	0·60 (say)	0·50
Workability	Low	Low
Aggregate/cement ratio	7·0	5·5

The relative materials' cost of these is about 108:100 in favour of the leaner mix. Good control, of course, costs money, but if poor control is due to inefficient use of supervision and/or plant then this is no less expensive than good control and the overall price of the concrete in the leaner mix may be significantly cheaper than the richer mix.

There are a number of ways of estimating the design mean strength to satisfy a specified characteristic strength; one may or may not have a choice as to which to adopt. Assuming that one has a choice, probably the most realistic way is that proposed by Erntroy,[23] who, as a result of a large-scale investigation into site cubes, concluded that the water/cement ratios required to give the design and characteristic strengths are proportional for any one standard of control. Thus:

$$\left(\frac{(w/c)\bar{\mu}}{(w/c)\mu_0} = \mathrm{K}\right)$$

where $(w/c)\bar{\mu}$ = water/cement ratio for design mean strength, $(w/c)\mu_0$ = water/cement ratio for characteristic strength, K = constant (called the control ratio) the value of which depends upon the level of control, $\bar{\mu}$ = design mean strength and μ_0 = characteristic strength.

Since $\bar{\mu} > \mu_0$, then

$$\left(\frac{w}{c}\right)\bar{\mu} < \left(\frac{w}{c}\right)\mu_0$$

Therefore K < 1.

The values of K have been determined according to the type of batching plant used, the level of supervision exercised and the percentage of cube results acceptable below the specified characteristic strength. Table 4.1 shows suggested values of control ratio for the various conditions. With sufficient experience of particular materials' supplies, levels of supervision attainable on contruction projects and accuracy of control associated with typical batching plants, these control ratios can readily be modified.

TABLE 4.1

Control ratios for different degrees of control

Batching of cement and aggregates	Supervision	Control ratio for characteristic strength based on cube defective rate of		
		5%	2·5%	1%
Very accurately controlled weigh-batching equipment	Poor	0·82	0·78	0·75
	Normal	0·85	0·82	0·79
	Good	0·88	0·86	0·84
Normal weigh-batching equipment	Poor	0·79	0·75	0·71
	Normal	0·83	0·78	0·76
	Good	0·86	0·83	0·81

Example

The following example illustrates this method:

(i) the specified characteristic strength (accepting 5% of the cube results below this) is 30 N/mm^2 at 28 days;

(ii) ordinary Portland cement is to be used;

(iii) normal weigh-batching equipment will be operated and normal supervision will be exercised.

From Fig. 4.1 it can be seen that the water/cement ratio required is about 0·65.

From Table 4.1 a control ratio of 0·83 is obtained.

The water/cement ratio for the design mean strength is therefore $0{\cdot}83 \times 0{\cdot}65 = 0{\cdot}54$.

The anticipated mean strength is, then, about 38 N/mm^2.

Had we assumed good supervision for the same concrete then the control ratio = 0·86. Therefore water/cement ratio for design mean strength $= 0{\cdot}86 \times 0{\cdot}65 = 0{\cdot}56$. Anticipated mean strength = 36 N/mm^2.

Whilst the former method proposed by Entroy would seem to be the most realistic, the simplest, and in practice probably the most widely used, method is to assume that there is a constant difference, for a given level of control, between the specified characteristic strength and the design mean strength:

$$\bar{\mu} = \mu_0 + K_1$$

where $\bar{\mu}$ = design mean strength, μ_0 = specified characteristic strength and K_1 = constant which is a function of the quality control (*see* Chapter 11 for more detailed information).

The value of this constant has been recommended[24] to be at least 7·5 N/mm^2 where there is previous data to support this value, and at least 15·0 N/mm^2 in the absence of such data, where about 5% cube defectives are anticipated.

Example

The specified characteristic strength is 30 N/mm^2 at 28 days. Ordinary Portland cement is to be used and good control will be assumed, supported by data from previous testing.

Design strength $= 30 + 7{\cdot}5 = 37{\cdot}5$ N/mm^2. From Fig. 4.1, water/cement ratio = 0·55.

With sufficient experience and data the values of the constant K may, of course, be chosen realistically.

4.2.3 The design mean strength as in Road Note No. 4[8]

Because the approach was rather different when Road Note No. 4 was produced, nomenclature and philosophy were not the same as they are at present. The concept of characteristic strength was not widely understood and the term 'minimum strength' was generally accepted. The statistical nature of the latter was seldom acknowledged.

Data in Road Note No. 4 were given as guidance in choosing the 'average strength' (*i.e.* the design mean strength) in order to satisfy the specified 'minimum strength' for different levels of control. The relations between these two was taken as:

$$\frac{\mu_0}{\bar{\mu}} = K_2$$

where $\bar{\mu}$ = the 'average strength', μ_0 = the 'minimum strength' and K_2 = constant factor, the value of which was dependent upon the level of quality control.

While this approach was useful (and is still used) it is not realistic for a wide range of strengths and levels of quality control and is not recommended in relevant codes of practice in the UK. It is not considered further here.

4.3 DURABILITY

As already stated, durability is extremely important and, in some instances, of prime importance. Since it depends upon the constitution of the concrete and on its environment we must be careful to bear this in mind and not to concentrate exclusively on strength. Usually there are requirements as to cement content and cover to steel reinforcement and, in some cases, to type of cement and to other special ingredients.

For reinforced concrete, typical minimum cement contents are 250 to 330 kg/m^3 for internal condition of exposure and 280 to 370 kg/m^3 for external conditions, the lower figure corresponding to non-corrosive or sheltered conditions and the higher to corrosive or severe conditions.

For special circumstances there will be other requirements, *e.g.* the use of sulphate-resisting cement[25] and the use of entrained air (*see* Chapter 8).

Nominal cover to reinforcement, generally from 40 mm to 15 mm depending upon the grade of concrete used, will be a deciding factor in the choice of maximum size of aggregate.

Reference should be made to the British Standard Code of Practice for the Structural Use of Concrete[24] for guidance on the selection of concrete for durability.

The mix having been chosen on the grounds of strength should be checked against the durability requirements and the higher cement content used in the mix proportioning. If, for example, a cement content of 240 kg/m^3 is required to satisfy the specified characteristic strength of a concrete used internally, subjected to corrosive conditions, then the latter would require a minimum cement content of, say, 330 kg/m^3 and this is the value that should be used unless previous experience has indicated otherwise.

4.4 WORKABILITY

The economics of concrete production are seriously affected by this important property of the plastic concrete; choosing the correct level of workability is therefore worthy of some attention. It is not possible to indicate the ideal level of workability for all circumstances since this depends upon the type of mixer, methods of transporting, placing, and compacting the concrete, as well as on the characteristics of the section to be cast. However, the following can be considered as a rough guide until full-scale conditions indicate otherwise:

TABLE 4.2

Suggested levels of workability for concretes for different uses

Workability	Suitable use	Compacting factor	Approximate slump (mm)	'V–B' (sec)
Very low	Section with easy access to vibration	0·78	0	15–30
Low	Simply reinforced section vibrated	0·85	0–50	8–12
Medium	More congested section vibrated	0·92	0–50	3–5
High	Heavily reinforced section vibrated	0·95	50–100	1–3

The values of compacting factor, slump and 'V–B' are approximate and are not directly comparable with each other over a wide range of mixes.

Some typical levels of workability for various concretes may be helpful in visualising the order of workability suitable for particular situations:

> concrete roads compacted by power-operated machines (*i.e.* with mechanical spreaders and powerful vibrating and finishing beams)—compacting factor 0·78 to 0·82;
> minor roads compacted with hand-operated vibrating beam—compacting factor about 0·88 to 0·92;
> minor roads compacted by hand-tamping beam—compacting factor about 0·92 to 0·95;
> mass concrete where, say, 3 in diameter poker vibrators can be used—compacting factor 0·78 to 0·82;
> awkwardly shaped beam with closely spaced reinforcement preventing use of poker vibrators; external type used—compacting factor 0·90 to 0·95;
> reinforced concrete columns, normal reinforcement allowing use of poker—compacting factor 0·88 to 0·92.

4.4.1 Effect of workability on aggregate/cement ratio

As can be seen from Fig. 4.3, for a given water/cement ratio the aggregate/cement ratio increases as the workability decreases; *e.g.*

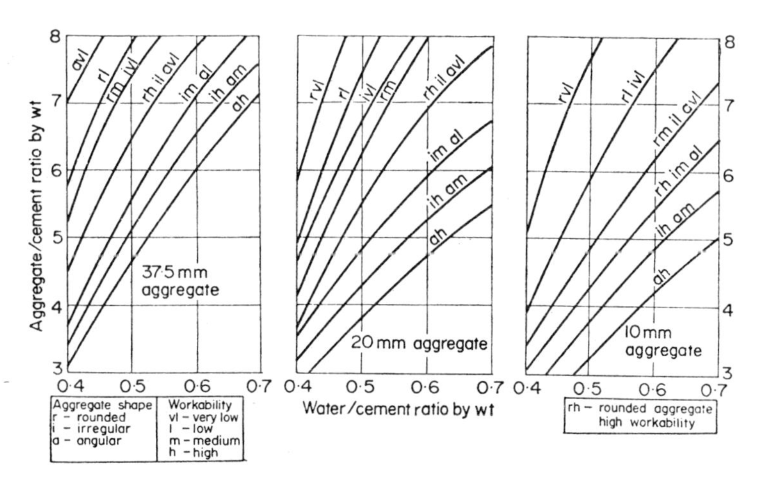

FIG. 4.3 Typical relations between aggregate/cement ratio (by weight), water/cement ratio and level of workability, for aggregates of different particle shape and maximum size: (a) 37·5 mm; (b) 20·0 mm; (c) 10·0 mm.

using 20 mm maximum size pit gravel and sand of irregular shape we obtain the following:

Water/cement ratio	Workability			
	Very low	Low	Medium	High
0·50	6·7	5·5	4·8	4·3
Relative cement content	100	116	128	138

There is a considerable increase in cement content as the mix becomes more workable and one might therefore be tempted into selecting the lowest level of workability on the grounds of economy. This is not the correct way to tackle the problem as it may lead to more expense in the end.

The total cost is the important factor and not just the cost of materials. Unless one has the plant capable of dealing with the chosen workability the costs incurred in placing, compacting, finishing and, possibly, making good, would outweigh the economic gain through using a leaner mix. If, on the other hand, one is unduly pessimistic, an unnecessarily rich mix will be selected, being wasteful in cement, though the actual site operation may be a good deal cheaper because of the higher workability. A realistic choice is necessary, comparable with the site conditions, *i.e.* suitable for the operations to be performed on the concrete and for the plant to be used, erring on the higher side of workability rather than risking the potentially costly effects of lack of it and bearing in mind that the final choice depends upon full-scale operations.

4.5 DATA FOR MIX PROPORTIONS

Figure 4.3(a), (b) and (c) shows approximate relations between aggregate/cement ratio, water/cement ratio and degree of workability for aggregates of 37·5 mm, 20·0 mm and 10·0 mm maximum particle size, each being of three types of particle shape (*i.e.* nominally rounded, irregular and angular).

These figures are based on data given in Road Note No. 4[8] and CACA Research Report No. 2;[9] the data have been condensed and slightly modified to enable a reduction to be made in the number of figures presented but it is considered that little, if any, loss of accuracy results from this. It should be noted that aggregates classed as rounded and irregular are assumed to have specific gravities of about 2·5 and 2·6 for the coarse and fine fractions respectively, while 2·7 is the appropriate density for the angular aggregate (both fractions). The aggregate/cement ratios given correspond to normally accepted sand contents required for stability (*see* Sections 2.6 and 4.6), *i.e.* about 35 to 45 % Zone 2 sand for the normal range of cement contents; more sand should be added for leaner mixes and less for

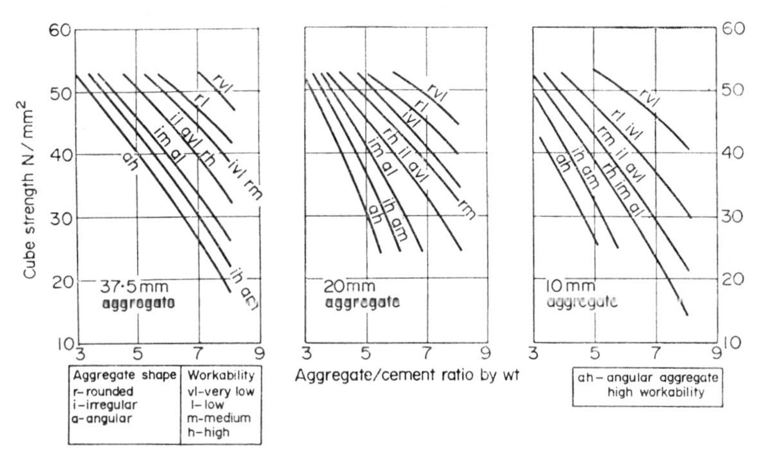

FIG. 4.4 Typical relations between cube strength, aggregate/cement ratio (by weight) and workability for aggregates of different particle shape and maximum size.

richer mixes, but this will not affect the chosen aggregate/cement ratio very much.

The data on rounded and angular aggregates of 37·5 mm maximum size are extrapolated from the published data in Road Note No. 4.

The description of aggregate particle shape applies to both coarse and fine fractions. Frequently combinations are used such that the overall grading is of mixed particle shape; for example, a crushed rock coarse aggregate is combined with a natural gravel sand. In such cases the data given do not apply directly but, nevertheless, may be used to provide a reasonable estimate of the required aggregate/cement ratio. This is illustrated by Examples 3 and 4 in Section 4.8.

Data are also presented in alternative forms in Figs. 4.4 and 4.5 showing relations between strength, aggregate/cement ratio and workability and between workability, water/cement ratio and aggregate/cement ratio respectively. Again, undue precision should not be attributed to these but they can be very useful in interpreting the results of trial mixes. It will be noticed that there is quite marked similarity between these various figures in terms of the general shape of the plotted curves and this phenomenon can be utilised in the mix design process.

A helpful guide to the classification of aggregates in terms of particle shape is that water-worn aggregates are usually rounded, pit gravels are usually of irregular shape and crushed rocks of angular shape.

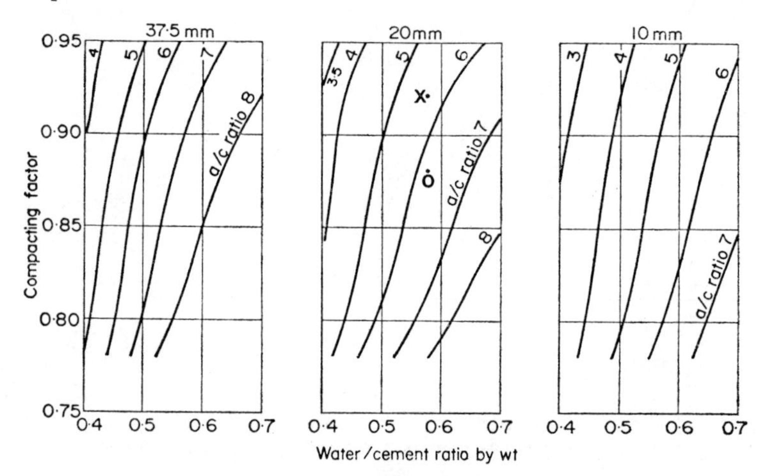

FIG. 4.5 Typical relations between compacting factor, water/cement ratio and aggregate/cement ratio (by weight), for a given particle shape.

4.6 STABILITY OF PLASTIC CONCRETE

There are various factors to be borne in mind as far as the stability of the mix is concerned. Different methods of transporting and placing will require varying degrees of stability; some structures will require more stable concrete than others; a change in the level of workability may induce instability in the mix, and so on. A few examples along these lines will illustrate the problem:

> concrete that is transported in open tippers, particularly over bumpy ground, is prone to segregation, unless the mix is sufficiently cohesive;

discharging the concrete down a chute or dropping it freely into a reinforced section, where it will bounce off the formwork and/or the reinforcement, will cause an incorrectly designed mix to segregate;

a high water content may result in a very fluid mortar which will be unstable;

a section, to be cast, with a high surface area to volume ratio (as, for example, an I-beam) or with a high percentage of reinforcement, will have a high 'mortar demand', as the available surfaces, whether of reinforcement or of the concrete section, will have to be coated with a skin of mortar;

sloping roofs without top shuttering and road slabs with cross-fall will require cohesive concrete that will not flow too readily.

4.6.1 Fixing the sand content

Having chosen the aggregate/cement ratio from Fig. 4.3, the next step is to fix the ratio of fine to coarse aggregate. This is linked with the question of stability. Since this property depends upon the amount and fluidity of the mortar we can see that with low cement contents we need more sand and with high cement contents we need

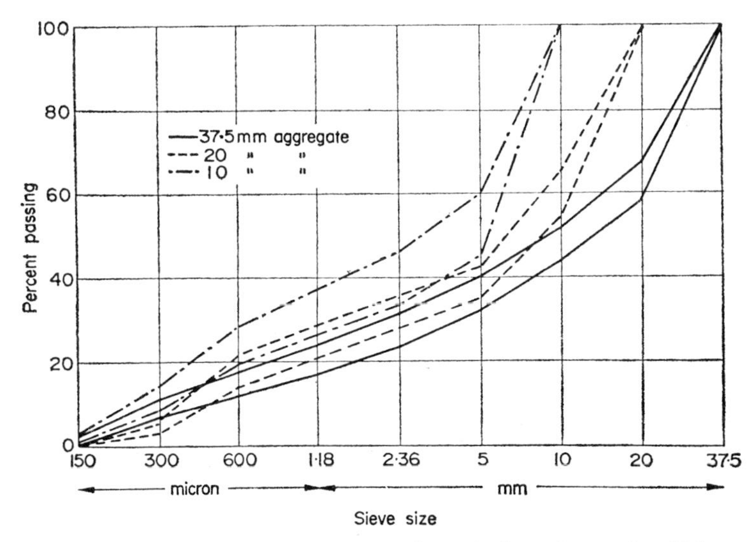

FIG. 4.6 Type gradings for aggregates of nominal maximum size 37·5 mm, 20·0 mm and 10·0 mm.

less sand. With high water contents—and therefore high workability—in a lean mix the mortar will be too fluid unless we add more sand; with a dry mix less sand is required.

For normal conditions, *i.e.* where the mix is neither very lean nor very rich (roughly between 250 and 400 kg of cement per cubic metre of compacted concrete), where the workability is not too high and where the circumstances do not require a particularly cohesive concrete, the overall aggregate grading may approximate to the grading curves shown in Fig. 4.6. These are based on the curves in Road Note No. 4[8] and CACA Research Report No. 2.[9] For 37·5 mm and 20 mm maximum size, this approximates to 35 to 40% of Zone 2 or coarse Zone 3 sand; for 10 mm maximum size it is about 40 to 45% sand.

If a Zone 1 sand were used this should be increased by about 5 to 10%, depending upon the coarseness; it should be decreased by about 10% for Zone 4 sands to obtain concretes of similar characteristics. For a better means of assessing the use of coarse and fine sands see Chapter 5.

Where the mix is rich the sand (Zone 2) can be reduced to about 30%; where it is lean 40 to 45% may be required. For high workability the sand should be increased to 45 to 50% for leaner and 35 to 40% for richer mixes.

Some examples at the end of this chapter (Section 4.8) will illustrate these points.

4.7 TRIAL MIXES

By its very nature the mix proportioning process must lead to trial mixes, because of the inability to be exact, inherent in the selection of aggregate/cement and water/cement ratios. Trial mixes enable one to make whatever adjustments are necessary.

The most realistic procedure, even for laboratory mixes, is to use wet, rather than dry, aggregates. On site this probably entails measuring the moisture contents of the aggregates and calculating the correct amount of 'free' water required in the mix. In the laboratory it is usual to have air-dried aggregates and these should be batched and soaked for about thirty minutes with sufficient water to bring them to the approximately saturated, surface-dry condition and then used in the mix. It will be appreciated that the correct water/cement ratio may not be precisely achieved by this approach but, on balance, it is better to accept this and have the other advantages which result from it.

It is very probable that the first trial mix will produce concrete which differs from that required in one or more ways; (a) it may be too cohesive or else not stable enough, (b) the workability may be incorrect and (c) the strength may be too high or too low. Each of these properties of the mix should be checked and the mix altered accordingly. The appearance of the plastic concrete should be noted and any necessary alterations can easily be decided upon, as pointed out in Chapter 2. With experience of mix design it is unlikely that the appearance will differ by much from that anticipated, at least as far as stability is concerned. It is much more likely that strength and/or workability will require modification.

Let us suppose that the following mix, using 20 mm maximum size pit gravel and Zone 2 pit sand, has been used as a trial: aggregate/cement ratio 5·5:1; 35% sand; water/cement ratio 0·50 to give a compacting factor 0·85 and compressive strength 31 N/mm^2 at 7 days, 42 N/mm^2 at 28 days.

The mix has reasonable stability but the compacting factor is 0·81, *i.e.* 0·04 less than required. Cubes from the mix indicate a 7-day strength of 34 N/mm^2. Referring to Fig. 4.1 we see that the water/cement ratio therefore required for 31 N/mm^2 is about 0·55. From Fig. 4.3(b) we can now work out our new aggregate/cement ratio and check the compacting factor and strength. We aim for a compacting factor 0·85 + 0·04 to allow for a drop of 0·04.

Water/cement ratio 0·55; aggregate/cement ratio 6·3 for compacting factor 0·85, 5·4 for compacting factor 0·92. Therefore aggregate/cement ratio required for compacting factor 0·89 is (5·4 + 6·3)/2 = 5·8.

Our new mix is therefore a 5·8:1. It is useful to check the water content per cubic metre of this mix (175 kg/m^3) then if a mix of similar workability is subsequently required, but with a 7-day mean strength of, say, 38 N/mm^2, this can be computed as follows.

From Fig. 4.1 we see that a water/cement ratio of 0·46 is necessary (for these materials):

$$\frac{\text{weight of water/m}^3}{\text{weight of cement/m}^3} = 0{\cdot}46$$

$$\text{weight of cement/m}^3 = \frac{\text{weight of water/m}^3}{0{\cdot}46}$$

$$= \frac{175\ \text{kg/m}^3}{0{\cdot}46}$$

$$= 380\ \text{kg/m}^3$$

If the specific gravity of the sand is 2·65 and the specific gravity of the gravel is 2·55, the mean specific gravity of the combined aggregate is (2·65 × 35%) + (2·55 × 65%) = 2·58.

Assuming no air voids in the compacted concrete:

$$\text{cement content (kg/m}^3) = \frac{1000}{(a/c)/2{\cdot}58 + (1/3{\cdot}12) + 0{\cdot}46}$$

$$380 = \frac{1000}{(a/c)/2{\cdot}58 + 0{\cdot}78}$$

$$a/c = \frac{704}{147}$$

$$= 4{\cdot}8$$

where a/c is the aggregate/cement ratio by weight.

An approximation to the above is given by (320/380) × 5·8 = 4·85, where 320 and 380 are the cement contents of the first and second mixes and 5·8 is the aggregate/cement ratio of the first mix.

4.8 EXAMPLES OF MIX DESIGN

Example 1

Concrete is required for a minor road which is considered not to need entrained air in it, where a small, hand-operated vibrating beam will be used to compact it. Normal site weigh-batching of cement and aggregates will be used and fair control. Twenty millimetre graded pit gravel and Zone 2 sand (of irregular shape) are available; ordinary Portland cement will be used. A characteristic strength of 20 N/mm^2 at 28 days is specified and available data indicates a likely margin of 15 N/mm^2 between characteristic and mean strengths.

(1) A suitable workability would be a compacting factor of about 0·92.

(2) On this project, a reasonable strength to aim for would be (20 + 15) N/mm^2. After control has been established this strength can be modified if the job goes on long enough to warrant it.

(3) From Fig. 4.1 we obtain a water/cement ratio of 0·58 (this should cause no worry as far as durability is concerned). See also Chapter 8 on air-entrained concrete.

(4) From Fig. 4.3(b) we abstract the following: water/cement ratio, 0·58; aggregate/cement ratio, 5·7.

(5) So that a good finish can readily be obtained, about 40% sand will be selected. This will also enable the concrete to be spread with less danger of separation.

(6) Mix proportions—1: 40% × 5·7: 60% × 5·7: water/cement ratio 0·58, *i.e.* 1:2·28:3·42:0·58.

If it is found that the concrete becomes rather difficult to finish—there may be tearing of the surface on the finishing pass of the beam—this may be due to an excess of 10–5 mm material in the graded aggregate. If so, either an alternative source of aggregate should be sought or instead of using the 20–5 mm material a single size 20–10 mm aggregate should be used.

The compacting factor 0·92 may not be suited to the particular vibrating beam in use, but this cannot be known without experience of this beam. It may be possible to decrease the workability to 0·88 compacting factor.

Then, from Fig. 4.3(b) we get:

water/cement ratio 0·58;
aggregate/cement ratio 6·8 for compacting factor 0·85;
aggregate/cement ratio 5·7 for compacting factor 0·92;
therefore use (6·8 + 5·7)/2 for compacting factor 0·88.

Figure 4.5(b) can be used likewise.

The point of intersection of lines drawn through a water/cement ratio of 0·58 and a compacting factor of 0·92 is 'X' and this represents the first mix, *i.e.* an aggregate/cement ratio of 5·8. The curve immediately to the right of that is then appropriate to an aggregate/cement ratio of 6·0 and the one next to that, on the right, is 7·0. Therefore, for a water/cement ratio of 0·58 and a compacting factor of 0·88 the point 'O' is correct and this represents an aggregate/cement ratio almost mid-way between 6·0 and 6·5, say 6·2.

Similarly Fig. 4.4(b) can be used.

Example 2

Concrete is required for reinforced concrete beams. The specified characteristic strength at 28 days is 30 N/mm^2. Good finish is essential; there is access for a 50 mm poker vibrator and 20 mm maximum size aggregate can be used. The materials available are 20 mm graded pit gravel and Zone 3 pit sand from a good source; ordinary Portland cement is to be used and supervision will be good.

(1) Workability: although it may be possible to cope with 'low' workability, since appearance is so important and to minimise labour requirements in placing the concrete, 'medium' workability will be chosen (*i.e.* a compacting factor of 0·92).

(2) Since supervision is good and aggregate supply is also good, the design mean strength should be (30 + 10) N/mm^2 unless there is evidence to the contrary (*see* Chapter 11 for statistical assessment).

(3) From Fig. 4.1 we obtain a water/cement ratio of 0·52.

(4) From Fig. 4.3(b) we get: water/cement ratio, 0·52; aggregate/cement ratio, 5·0; compacting factor, 0·92.

(5) Bearing in mind that finish is important and that the sand is Zone 3, as a first guess we can assume about 38% sand.

(6) Mix proportions: 1:1·9:3·1:water/cement ratio 0·52.

Example 3

Concrete is required for precast units, with excellent batching plant available and good supervision expected. The specified characteristic strength at 28 days is 37·5 N/mm^2 (using ordinary Portland cement) and 2·5% cubes are allowed to fall below this. The aggregates are 20 mm and 10 mm single size crushed granite and Zone 2 natural pit sand. The compaction of the concrete will be by intensive vibration techniques and it will be transported in dumpers a distance of about 50 m.

(1) The workability can be tentatively chosen at about 0·82 compacting factor (this may well be lowered subsequently).

(2) Using the control ratio method we see from Table 4.1 that the control ratio corresponding to the supposed conditions is 0·86 for 2·5% cube results allowed to fall below the specified characteristic strength.

(3) The water/cement ratio for 37·5 N/mm^2 at 28 days using ordinary Portland cement is 0·56 (from Fig. 4.1).

(4) The water/cement ratio for mean strength = 0·56 × 0·86 = 0·48. The anticipated mean strength = 45 N/mm^2 (this is acceptable).

(5) From Fig. 4.3(b) (for a water/cement ratio of 0·48):

Aggregate/ cement ratio	Com- pacting factor	Aggregate type
5·1	0·78	Angular coarse and fine
4·5	0·85	Angular coarse and fine
4.8	0·82	Angular coarse and fine
6·3	0·78	Irregular coarse and fine
5·1	0·85	Irregular coarse and fine
5·7	0·82	Irregular coarse and fine
$\frac{4·8 + 5·7}{2}$ = 5·3	0·82	Angular coarse and irregular fine

Allowing for the fact that the sand has a greater effect on workability we could probably increase this aggregate/cement ratio to about 5·5:1.

(6) The compacting equipment used may easily cope with a low sand content, but the shape of the precast unit and the disposition of reinforcement may require careful consideration. Taking 35% sand therefore seems reasonable and dividing the 20 mm and 10 mm aggregates as 2:1 we can fix the mix proportions as in (7).

(7) 1:35% × 5·5:22% × 5·5:43% × 5·5:0·48, *i.e.* 1:1·92:1·21: 2·57:0·48.

If the workability were reduced to, say, very low, the sand might be reduced to about 32% and the aggregate/cement ratio increased to about 5·8:1.

Example 4

Assuming the same concrete is required as for Example 3 but normal weigh-batching of cement and aggregates is to be used and good supervision:

(1) Control ratio from Table 4.1 = 0·83.

(2) Water/cement ratio for mean = 0·56 × 0·83 = 0·46.

(3) From Fig. 4.3(b) (for a water/cement ratio of 0·46):

Aggregate/ cement ratio	Compacting factor	Aggregate type
4·7	0·78	Angular coarse and fine
4·3	0·85	Angular coarse and fine
4·5	0·82	Angular coarse and fine
5·9	0·78	Irregular coarse and fine
4·7	0·85	Irregular coarse and fine
5·3	0·82	Irregular coarse and fine
$\frac{4{\cdot}5 + 5{\cdot}3}{2} = 4{\cdot}9$	0·82	Angular coarse and irregular fine

Example 5

In-situ concrete is required between precast roof units. The specified characteristic strength at 28 days is 35 N/mm^2. The sections are heavily congested and small, restricting aggregate to 10 mm maximum size. Because the volume of *in-situ* concrete is extremely small, assume fair control. Rounded gravel and sand (Zone 3) are available.

(1) Workability: medium/high seems reasonable.

(2) Design mean strength, say (35 + 15) N/mm^2. Water/cement ratio from Fig. 4.1 = 0·42.

(3) From Fig. 4.3(c): water/cement ratio = 0·42; aggregate/cement ratio = 3·7 for compacting factor 0·92 and 3·3 for compacting factor 0·95.

Mix is therefore 3·5:1.

With Zone 3 sand and such a high cement content the sand content would normally be reduced to perhaps 25%; in this case, because the workability is rather high it may be desirable to use 30%. This is best decided after observing the behaviour of the first few batches of concrete.

Since the volume of concrete required is so small, whether the richer mix is used or not will hardly affect overall costs and it may well facilitate the site production.

Example 6

Let us suppose that we are using aggregates that have specific gravities of 2·70 and 2·60 for the fine and coarse fractions respectively.

The mix, based on Fig. 4.3, is assumed to be 1:6·2 with 35% sand, water/cement ratio 0·55. How would we modify this to suit our aggregates with different specific gravities?

(1) 1:35% × 6·2:65% × 6·2, *i.e.* 1:2·17:4·03, cement:fine aggregate:coarse aggregate.

(2) The specific gravities of the aggregates assumed in Fig. 4.3 are 2·60 and 2·50 for the fine and coarse types respectively.

(3) The absolute volume of sand required in the mix is therefore 2·17/2·60 absolute volume units.

(4) If y is the proportion of sand by weight in the modified mix, then the absolute volume = $y/2{\cdot}70$.

(5) $(y/2{\cdot}70) = (2{\cdot}17/2{\cdot}60)$. Therefore $y = (2{\cdot}17 \times 2{\cdot}70)/2{\cdot}60$, *i.e.* the proportion of sand in the modified mix is the proportion of sand in the original mix multiplied by the ratio of the two specific gravities. Likewise for the coarse aggregate.

(6) Mix proportions are: 1:2·17 × (2·70/2·60):4·03 × (2·60/2·50): 0·55, *i.e.* 1:2·26:4·19:0·55.

This ensures that both sets of proportions will have similar cement contents, which is the main object of the exercise. The aggregate/cement ratio is just a convenient way of expressing the mix for batching purposes but need not be truly indicative of cement content if aggregates of different types and from various sources are considered. One must therefore be careful to ensure that the mix design data are applicable to the materials to be used; if the specific gravities are significantly different then allowance, as above, must be made for this in the proportions expressed by weight.

Chapter 5

METHODS OF COMBINING AGGREGATES TO OBTAIN DESIRED GRADINGS

5.1 INTRODUCTION

In Chapter 4 grading curves are suggested, for 37·5 mm, 20 mm and 10 mm maximum size aggregates, which may be suitable for concretes that are not required to be especially cohesive. Assuming that one decides to approximate to these the problem then becomes an arithmetical·one of computing the proportions of fine to coarse aggregate which will yield the required grading. This is nothing more than an arithmetical exercise and does not mean that the chosen grading is a satisfactory one for the particular circumstances; it is a check on the arithmetic and not on the suitability of the mix.

There are two methods of tackling the problem, one graphical and the other arithmetical. Both can be used with what we may term 'normally' graded aggregates, but the latter is better when the aggregates are, for example, a rather fine sand plus coarse aggregate. The former can be used to combine any number of aggregates together, the latter only two.

5.2 GRAPHICAL METHOD

Let us suppose that we have the following sieve analysis of available aggregates:

	Sieve size							
	20·0 mm	10·0 mm	5·0 mm	2·36 mm	1·18 mm	600 μ	300 μ	150 μ
	91	3						
Percent passing	100	87	9					
		100	100	83	67	45	8	1

Our problem is how to combine a nominally single-size 20·0 mm aggregate plus a 10·0 mm aggregate plus a sand so that we get an overall grading which is within the following envelope (from Fig. 4.6):

	Sieve size							
	20·0 mm	10·0 mm	5·0 mm	2·36 mm	1·18 mm	600 μ	300 μ	150 μ
Percent passing	100	55–65	35–42	28–35	21–28	14–21	3–5	0–1
Centre of envelope	100	60	38	31	24	17	4	1

Figure 5.1 shows the procedure. On the left-hand ordinate mark out a scale representing percent passing each sieve size. Draw a line AB at any angle to the horizontal but such that the length of AC, along the horizontal axis, is not too short. AB represents our desired grading. Since we want 100% passing the 20·0 mm sieve, where AB intersects a horizontal through the 100% level on our percent passing scale this is a point on the ordinate representing the 20·0 mm sieve;

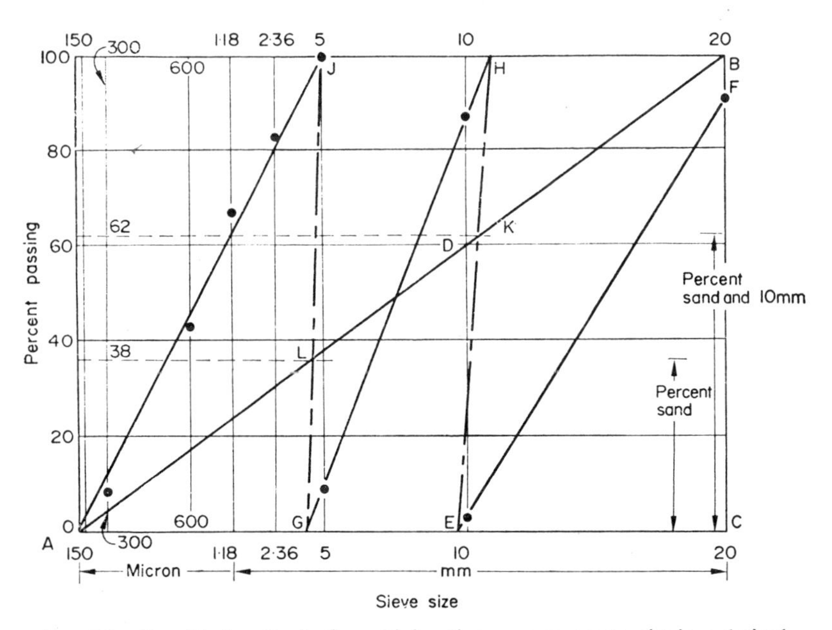

FIG. 5.1 Graphical method of combining three aggregates to obtain a desired overall grading.

draw a vertical through this to intersect the horizontal through A, at C, and we now have a 20·0 mm ordinate, BC. Likewise, we require 60% passing the 10·0 mm sieve, so we draw a horizontal through 60% on the percent passing scale and where that intersects AB—at D—we draw a vertical and this is our 10·0 mm ordinate. And so on for all the other sizes until we have constructed a sieve size scale on AC. All we have done is use a straight line (AB) as our overall grading and construct a sieve size scale to suit it, the scale being graduated in unequal increments; this is distinct from Fig. 4.6 where our sieve size scale is constructed first of equal increments and then our overall grading is plotted which becomes non-linear in form.

On our graph we can now plot the available aggregates. We then draw 'best-fit' lines through these points; in this case there is no difficulty with the (20·0–10·0 mm) and (10·0–5·0 mm) material as there are only two points on each, but with the sand we have six points. Where the sand grading is such that the points naturally tend to fall on a straight line—as they do here—this graphical method can be used quite successfully. AJ is the sand grading, GH the (10·0–5·0 mm) and EF the (20·0–10·0 mm) size. Join E and H, intersecting AB at K. Join G and J, intersecting AB at L. L represents the sand fraction of our mix; on our percent passing scale this is 38%. K represents the sand plus 10·0 mm aggregate, which is 62% on our scale; therefore the amount of 10·0 mm aggregate is (62 − 38)% = 24%. The amount of 20·0 mm aggregate is (100 − 62)% = 38%.

Next we check the arithmetic as follows:

	Sieve size							
	20·0 mm	10·0 mm	5·0 mm	2·36 mm	1·18 mm	600 μ	300 μ	150 μ
38% of 20·0 mm material	35	1						
24% of 10·0 mm material	24	21	2					
38% sand	38	38	38	31	25	17	3	0
Combined	97	60	40	31	25	17	3	0
Required	100	60	38	31	24	17	4	1

Let us suppose that we are going to use a (20·0–5·0 mm) graded coarse aggregate plus a sand, the sieve analysis being as follows:

	Sieve size							
	20·0 mm	10·0 mm	5·0 mm	2·36 mm	1·18 mm	600 μ	300 μ	150 μ
Percent passing	95	40	5					
		100	100	80	62	40	10	2

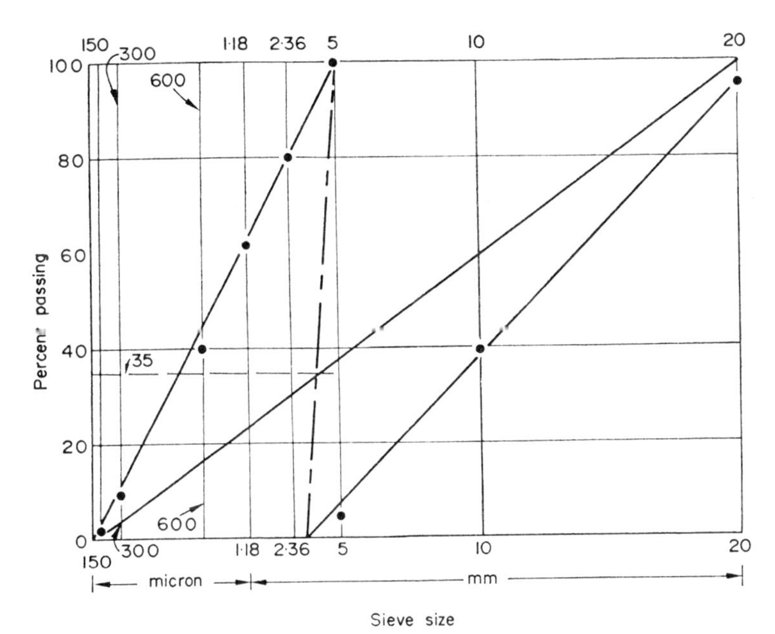

FIG. 5.2 Graphical method of combining a fine aggregate and a graded coarse aggregate.

From Fig. 5.2 we see that we require 35% sand and 65% coarse aggregate; checking the arithmetic we get:

	Sieve size							
	20·0 mm	10·0 mm	5·0 mm	2·36 mm	1·18 mm	600 μ	300 μ	150 μ
65% coarse	62	26	3					
35% sand	35	35	35	28	22	14	3	1
Combined	97	61	38	28	22	14	3	1
Required	100	60	38	31	24	17	4	1

5.2.1 Limitation of graphical method

The following example will illustrate the limitation of the graphical method. The available aggregates have these gradings:

	Sieve size							
	20·0 mm	10·0 mm	5·0 mm	2·36 mm	1·18 mm	600 μ	300 μ	150 μ
	95	5						
Percent passing	100	90	6					
		100	100	100	100	93	30	10

Plotting these on Fig. 5.3 shows the sand grading to be quite non-linear and it is extremely difficult to draw a 'best-fit' line through the points. The best fit line should be drawn so that the line joining its upper end to the lower end of the next line (*e.g.* the points J and G in Fig. 5.1) is as nearly vertical as possible. In the present case this line is well out of vertical. However, proceeding, we see that we

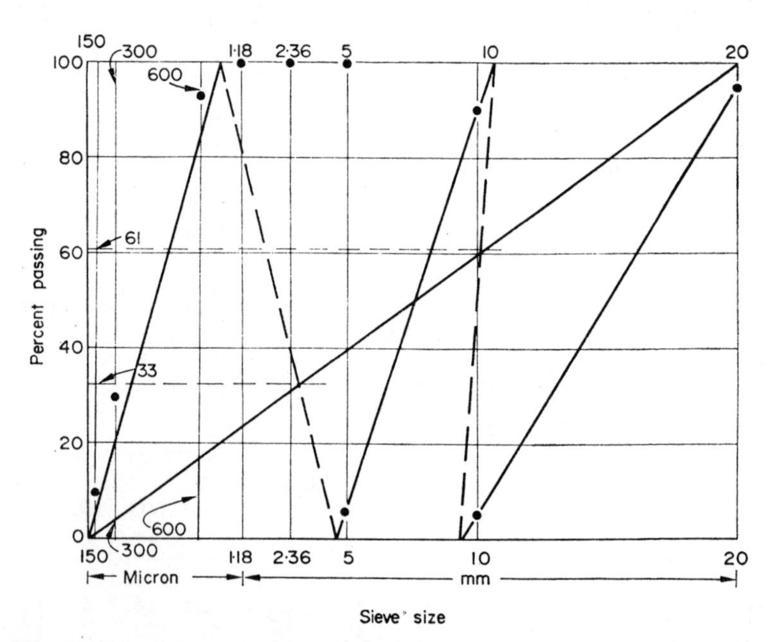

Fig. 5.3 Example illustrating limitation of the graphical method of combining aggregates.

require 33% sand, 28% (10–5·0 mm) aggregate and 39% (20·0–10·0 mm) aggregate. Working out the arithmetic we get our combined grading:

	Sieve size							
	20·0 mm	10·0 mm	5·0 mm	2·36 mm	1·18 mm	600 μ	300 μ	150 μ
Percent passing	98	60	35	33	33	31	10	3

This is very different from what we require in the finer sizes—the 1·18 mm, 600 and 300 μ sieves—and we must attempt the problem in a different way. This we can do by the 'arithmetical method'.

5.3 ARITHMETICAL METHOD

The basis of this method is the specific surface concept already mentioned in Chapter 2. This implies that the overall grading can change considerably but if the total specific surface of the aggregates remains constant then concretes with mutually similar properties will be produced. Since it is a comparatively difficult matter to measure specific surface we side-step this direct approach and use surface area indices instead. These are arbitrary numerical values attached to material between each successive pair of sieves, the values representing the surface areas—and thus, indirectly, the specific surface, since the specific gravity of normal aggregates hardly varies significantly with particle size—and therefore as the sieve size is more or less halved with each decremental size (37·5 mm, 20·0 mm, 10·0 mm, etc.) the surface area index should double (*see* page 18, Chapter 2). This assumes that the particle shape remains constant right down the grading scale, an assumption that does not conform with reality but is convenient nevertheless. If we let the (37·5–20·0 mm) size material have an index of 1, the (20·0–10·0 mm) material should be 2, the (10·0–5·0 mm) material should be 4, the (5·0–2·36 mm) material should be 8, and so on. This brings us to 128 for the (300–150 μ) size and the arithmetical computation becomes more unwieldy. It is therefore advantageous to start with a fractional index, *e.g.* $\frac{1}{8}$, but, of course, this is quite arbitrary and is a matter of personal choice.

An important point to note in this method is that material passing the 300 and 150 μ sieves is given the same surface area index.

Let us try the previous problem with this method. We first select the grading to which we want to approximate (this we have already done). Then we allocate the indices to the various amounts of each size in this grading and, by summation, compute the overall surface area index of the complete grading. This is therefore what we are trying to reproduce with our available aggregates. Having the sieve analyses of these, we can compute their surface area indices and determine the proportion of each necessary to give a combined index equal to that we require. Table 5.1 shows the procedure.

TABLE 5.1

1 Sieve sizes (mm or μ)	2 Surface area index value	3 Required grading	4 Surface area index required	5 Available aggregates		6 Available surface area index	
				Fine	Coarse	Fine	Coarse
20·0–10·0	$\frac{1}{8}$	40	5		37		5
10·0–5·0	$\frac{1}{4}$	22	5		58		14
5·0–2·36	$\frac{1}{2}$	7	4		4		2
2·36–1·18	1	7	7				
1·18–600	2	7	14	7		14	
600–300	4	13	52	63		252	
Passing 300	8	4	32	30		240	
			1·19			5·06	0·21

Let x = percent of sand in the mix. Then

$$1{\cdot}19 = \frac{x}{100} \times 5{\cdot}06 + \frac{(100 - x)}{100} 0{\cdot}21$$

$$119 = 5{\cdot}06x + 0{\cdot}21(100 - x)$$

$$x = \frac{98}{4{\cdot}85} \simeq 20\%$$

Therefore we require 20% sand and 80% coarse aggregate. The grading thus obtained will be:

	Sieve size							
	20·0 mm	10·0 mm	5·0 mm	2·36 mm	1·18 mm	600 μ	300 μ	150 μ
Percent passing	98	70	23	20	20	19	6	2

which is, of course, quite different from the actual grading required but will produce concrete with more or less the same properties.

Some comments on the various columns in Table 5.1 may clarify the method. Column 2 contains the surface indices allotted to each size, noting that the material passing the 300 and 150 μ sieves is grouped together. Column 3 is derived from our required grading and shows the percent contained between each successive pair of sieve sizes (thus, as there is 100% passing the 20·0 mm sieve and 60% passing the 10·0 mm sieve, there must be 40% retained on the 10·0 mm sieve; with 60% passing the 10·0 mm sieve and 38% passing the 5·0 mm sieve, there is 22% retained on the 5·0 mm sieve). Column 4 is the product of Columns 2 and 3 to the nearest whole number. In Column 5 we have our available aggregates and here we have to combine our (20·0–10·0 mm) size with our (10·0–5·0 mm) size before we can proceed, since the method can deal with only two aggregates altogether. It matters very little what combination we use as this effects the final result only very slightly, but we may take a 2:1 or even 3:1 ratio for 20·0:10·0 mm size. Taking a 2:1 ratio we compute the grading of the combined coarse aggregates and then fill in Column 5. Note also that the 1% retained on the 20·0 mm sieve has been ignored as it is of no consequence. Column 6 is the product of Columns 2 and 5.

As the figures in Columns 3 and 5 are percentages their indices' summations must be divided by 100, it being more convenient to do it then than for each individual figure. Therefore the 119 becomes 1·19 and 506 and 21 become 5·06 and 0·21.

It may be useful to do one of the other problems by this method. Let us take the (20·0–10·0 mm) graded coarse aggregate used in Fig. 5.2. Table 5.2 shows the procedure.

TABLE 5.2

1 Sieve sizes (mm or μ)	2 Surface area index value	3 Required grading	4 Surface area index required	5 Available aggregates Fine	Coarse	6 Available surface area index Fine	Coarse
20·0–10·0	$\frac{1}{8}$	40	5		55		7
10·0–5·0	$\frac{1}{4}$	22	5		35		9
5·0–2·36	$\frac{1}{2}$	7	4	20	5	10	2
2·36–1·18	1	7	7	18		18	
1·18–600	2	7	14	22		44	
600–300	4	13	52	30		120	
Passing 300	8	4	32	10		80	
			1·19			2·72	0·18

$$119 = 2{\cdot}72 + 0{\cdot}18\,(100 - x) \quad \text{where } x = \text{percent sand}$$

$$x = 40\%$$

Our overall grading is then:

	Sieve size 20·0 mm	10·0 mm	5·0 mm	2·36 mm	1·18 mm	600 μ	300 μ	150 μ
Percent passing	97	64	43	32	25	16	4	1

which is slightly different from our previous example but, again, will produce concrete of the same characteristics.

It will be found that if this method is used with very fine sands then, as a result of the dominant emphasis given to the finer particles in computing the surface area index, absurdly low sand contents may be arrived at. Common sense should always prevail and, as a general guide, for most concretes 20% should be taken as the minimum permissible sand content; with less than this amount there are severe practical problems with the production of the concrete.

5.4 MURDOCK'S METHOD OF MIX DESIGN

There is some connection between this and the arithmetical method just dealt with but the former includes other factors which affect workability and is an attempt to rationalise mix design. Workability is related, by Murdock's method, to particle shape and size distribution, and to mix proportions, and he proposes a means whereby a numerical evaluation of these factors is possible.

5.4.1 Surface index (f_s)

Experimental rather than theoretical values of these are suggested, many mixes having been analysed and values having been evolved by a process of successive approximation.[13] These values are shown in Table 5.3.

TABLE 5.3

Sieve sizes (mm or μ)	Surface index (f_s) for particles between sieve sizes[13]
37·5–20·0	−2
20·0–10·0	−1
10·0–5·0	1
5·0–2·36	4
2·36–1·18	7
1·18–600	8
600–300	9
300–150	7
Passing 150	1

A most interesting aspect of these surface indices is that they do not double as the sieve size decreases; they reach a peak at the 1·18 mm–600 μ size and the material passing a 150 μ sieve has a very low index. In order to counterbalance the negative values obtained with the coarse sizes an arbitrary constant of 330 is added during the computation of the overall surface index for any one grading. For convenience, this value is then divided by 1 000. An example of this is given later (*see* page 71).

5.4.2 Particle shape

As pointed out in Chapter 2, the angularity number test has enabled a numerical assessment to be made of particle shape. Murdock uses this in a modified form which is called the angularity index:

$$f_a = \frac{3f_h}{20} + 1{\cdot}0$$

where f_a = angularity index and f_h = angularity number.

Values of angularity index are suggested for various aggregates as in Table 5.4.

TABLE 5.4

Type of coarse aggregate	Source	Angularity index, f_a
Quartisite gravel, natural	Bridport	1·15
Flint gravel, natural	Chertsey	1·9
Limestone, crushed	Mendips	2·05
Crush granites and basalts, and crushed Chertsey flint gravel	Various	2·2–2·5

The angularity indices which Murdock adopted for comparison with Road Note No. 4[8] are shown in Table 5.5.

In establishing a mathematical relation between workability and the various influencing factors, it was found that as far as grading and shape were concerned this was best dealt with through one parameter, namely the products of the two ($f_s f_a$).

TABLE 5.5

Type of aggregate	Angularity index, f_a
Rounded (Bridport) coarse aggregate	1·15
Fine aggregate	1·80
Irregular (London river gravel and sand)	1·90
Granite, crushed (coarse and fine aggregate)	2·35

5.4.3 Water content

The amount of water necessary to 'wet' the cement was determined experimentally: this is the amount that causes a sudden increase in workability of the cement paste and varied from a water/cement ratio of 0·23 to 0·29. A value of 0·25 is suggested as being a reasonable figure (if necessary a simple test will indicate the correct figure for the particular cement in use). The water content, for workability, is therefore based on (water/cement ratio—0·25).

The water/cement ratio is that based on saturated, surface-dry aggregates and this means adding the necessary water to the dry aggregates (if used) about half an hour before mixing. This is essential as the effects of absorption are an unnecessary complicating factor.

5.4.4 Cement content

As the cement content increases, the effect of grading and shape of aggregates becomes less important and analysis shows that when the aggregate/cement ratio (by absolute volume) is 2 these effects are negligible. The aggregate/cement ratio is then taken to have a 'datum' of $(Av - 2)$, where Av = aggregate/cement ratio by absolute volume, in order to plot the various factors against workability and establish a numerical relation between them:

$$CF = 0{\cdot}74\left(\frac{10(w/c - 0{\cdot}25)}{f_s f_a (Av - 2)} + 0{\cdot}67\right)$$

where CF = compacting factor, w/c = free water/cement ratio, f_s = surface index of overall aggregate grading, f_a = angularity index of overall aggregate grading and Av = aggregate/cement ratio by absolute volume.

$$Av = \frac{\text{absolute volume of aggregates}}{\text{absolute volume of cement}}$$

$$= \frac{\text{weight of aggregates}}{\text{specific gravity of aggregates}} \times \frac{\text{specific gravity of cement}}{\text{weight of cement}}$$

$$= \frac{3{\cdot}15 Wa}{Wc \times Ga}$$

where Wa = weight of aggregates, Wc = weight of cement, Ga = specific gravity of aggregates and 3·15 is taken as the specific gravity of Portland cement.

5.4.5 Mix design

(1) The water/cement ratio is fixed from strength and durability considerations.

(2) Determine f_s and f_a. Suggested values for f_s:

37·5 mm	maximum size	$f_s = 0{\cdot}55$
20·0 mm	maximum size	$f_s = 0{\cdot}60$
10·0 mm	maximum size	$f_s = 0{\cdot}70$

Where aggregates are particularly uniform these values may be reduced by up to 0·05; where less uniform than normal they should be increased.

From sieve analyses of coarse and fine aggregates available the f_s of each can be determined and the percentage of sand calculated to give the total f_s equal to that required (as in Section 5.3).

f_a can be measured or assumed from data given.

(3) Determine

$$\frac{w/c - 0{\cdot}25}{f_s f_a}$$

(4) Use Fig. 5.4 to determine the aggregate/cement ratio by absolute volume for a particular compacting factor.

(5) Aggregate/cement ratio by weight is $(Av \times Ga)/3{\cdot}15$.

Examples of use of this method

(a) Determine the f_s of the grading envelope shown in Fig. 4.6 for 20·0 mm maximum size aggregate.

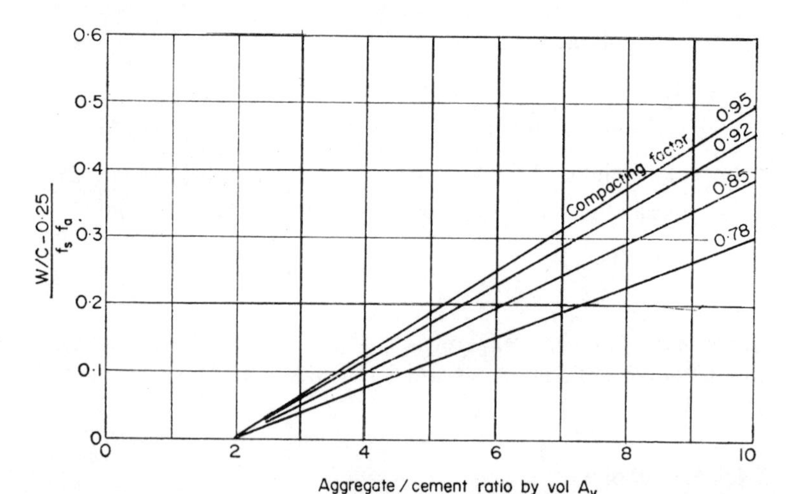

FIG. 5.4 Relation between compacting factor, water/cement ratio, surface and angularity indices and aggregate/cement ratio (based on Ref. 13).

Sieve sizes (mm or μ)	f_s	Percent between sieves Coarser grading	Percent between sieves Finer grading	f_s Coarser grading	f_s Finer grading
20·0–10·0	−1	45	35	−45	−35
10·0–5·0	1	20	23	20	23
5·0–2·36	4	7	7	28	28
2·36–1·18	7	7	7	49	49
1·18–600	9	7	7	63	63
600–300	9	11	16	99	144
300–150	7	3	5	21	35
Passing 150	1	0	0	0	0
				235	307
				+330	+330
				565	637

The constant 330 is added to the summated f_s value and this is then divided by 1 000; 565 becomes 0·565 and 637 becomes 0·637.

(b) Use of trial mix to determine f_a.
Aggregate/cement ratio by weight = 6:1.
35% sand; water/cement ratio 0·55; average specific gravity 2·50.

$$Av = \frac{6 \times 3{\cdot}15}{2{\cdot}50 \times 1} = 7{\cdot}55$$

Compacting factor from trial mix = 0·85.
Therefore, from Fig. 5.4

$$\frac{w/c - 0{\cdot}25}{f_s f_a} = 0{\cdot}26$$

$$f_s f_a = \frac{0{\cdot}30}{0{\cdot}26} = 1{\cdot}15$$

If $f_s = 0{\cdot}60$ (from grading and surface indices), therefore

$$f_a = \frac{1{\cdot}15}{0{\cdot}60} = 1{\cdot}92$$

This figure can then be used for further mixes with these aggregates and grading.

(c) Mix required to satisfy the following criteria:

28-day compressive strength = 33 N/mm^2.

Ordinary Portland cement is to be used and irregular gravel and sand, 20·0 mm maximum size, with the following gradings:

	Sieve size							
	20·0 mm	10·0 mm	5·0 mm	2·36 mm	1·18 mm	600 μ	300 μ	150 μ
Percent passing	98	35	3					
		100	100	85	67	45	20	5

Specific gravities of fine and coarse aggregates 2·65 and 2·55 respectively. Compacting factor 0·85.

(1) Water/cement ratio = 0·61 (from Fig. 4.1).

(2) f_a = 1·90 (assumed).

(3) f_s required to be 0·60.

Sieve sizes (mm or μ)	f_s	Percent retained between sieves		f_s	
		Fine	Coarse	Fine	Coarse
37·5–20·0	−2		2		−4
20·0–10·0	−1		63		−63
10·0–5·0	1		32		32
5·0–2·36	4	13	3	52	12
2·36–1·18	7	18		126	
1·18–600	9	22		198	
600–300	9	25		225	
300–150	7	15		105	
Passing 150	1	5		5	
				711	−23
				+330	+330
				1 041	307

Dividing by 1 000, f_s = 1·041 and 0·307 for fine and coarse aggregates respectively.

Let x = percent sand. Then

$$0{\cdot}60 = (x \times 1{\cdot}041) + (100 - x)\,0{\cdot}307$$
$$60 = 1{\cdot}04x + 30{\cdot}7 - 0{\cdot}31x$$
$$x = 40\%\text{ sand}$$

(4)

$$\frac{w/c - 0{\cdot}25}{f_s f_a} = \frac{0{\cdot}61 - 0{\cdot}25}{0{\cdot}60 \times 1{\cdot}90} = \frac{0{\cdot}36}{1{\cdot}14} = 0{\cdot}315$$

(5) From Fig. 5.4, $Av = 8{\cdot}5$.

(6) Aggregate/cement ratio by weight = $8{\cdot}5\ Ga/3{\cdot}15$.

$$Ga = (40 \times 2{\cdot}65) + (60 \times 2{\cdot}55) = 1{\cdot}06 + 1{\cdot}53 = 2{\cdot}59$$

$$\text{Aggregate/cement ratio by weight} = \frac{8{\cdot}5 \times 2{\cdot}59}{3{\cdot}15} = 7$$

(7) Final mix proportions are 1:2·8:4·2, water/cement ratio 0·61.

5.5 CONCLUSION

It cannot be emphasised too much that methods of combining aggregates to achieve a desired grading are a very minor part of concrete mix design. They are a convenient way of tackling some arithmetic but they say nothing at all about the correctness of the choice of materials to be used.

Of the three approaches shown, that proposed by Murdock is probably the most realistic and rational. However, for the usual ranges of aggregate gradings used, similar answers will be given by each method; where the graphical method is not applicable, for example, because of the particle size distribution of the sand, either of the other two should give a reasonable answer. It should be noted that if the answer found, by whatever method, is nonsensical then it should be treated as a nonsense and an informed, intuitive assessment made instead.

Chapter 6

GAP-GRADED CONCRETE

6.1 CONTINUOUS AND GAP-GRADINGS

In concrete using normally graded aggregates there are usually particles in all size ranges from the coarsest to the finest, *i.e.* the grading is continuous from the largest size to the material passing a 150 μ sieve. For example:

	Sieve size							
	20·0 mm	10·0 mm	5·0 mm	2·36 mm	1·18 mm	600 μ	300 μ	150 μ
Percent passing	100	55	35	28	21	14	3	0

With some aggregates it is possible to produce gradings that have particles missing in one or more of the sizes. For example:

	Sieve size							
	20·0 mm	10·0 mm	5·0 mm	2·36 mm	1·18 mm	600 μ	300 μ	150 μ
Percent passing	99	70	23	20	20	19	6	2

The former is termed a 'continuous' grading and the latter a 'gap' grading.

Gap-graded concrete is neither new nor uniquely difficult, though some problems in controlling mixes on site have led to the belief that unique skills are required to produce good concrete when using gap-graded aggregates. Good control is essential—and there is far less room for mistakes than with continuously-graded aggregates—but this requires care and good supervision, nothing more.

6.2 TWO APPROACHES TO GAP-GRADED CONCRETE

There are two approaches to the design of gap-graded concrete; one uses the specific surface concept dealt with in Chapter 5; the other is an attempt to predict the packing arrangement of the coarse aggregate in the mould to be concreted and then to deduce the amount of mortar required to fill the voids available.

6.2.1 Particle-packing

Taking the latter method, the following is the suggested procedure, based on work done by Stewart.[(4)] Let us suppose we have a container of unit volume which we want to fill with concrete. This concrete will be composed of water, cement and aggregates in certain proportions (assuming zero air voids).

Let A = absolute volume of aggregates, C = absolute volume of cement and W = absolute volume of water.

Then the volume of our container (equal, of course, to the volume of concrete) is $A + C + W$. We assume, in this method of design, that:

(i) the bulk volume of the coarse aggregate is equal to the volume of compacted concrete required;

(ii) the absolute volume of (water + cement mixture) is equal to (absolute volume of water) + (absolute volume of cement).

Let da = the specific gravity of the aggregate, dc = the specific gravity of the cement, Y = the aggregate/cement ratio by weight and X = the water/cement ratio by weight. Then the bulk density of the combined aggregate

$$= \frac{\text{weight}}{\text{volume}}$$

$$= \frac{Ada}{A + C + W} \tag{1}$$

$$Y = \frac{Ada}{Cdc} \tag{2}$$

Therefore

$$Ada = YCdc$$

$$X = \frac{W}{Cdc}$$

Therefore

$$W = XCdc$$

$$\frac{Ada}{A + C + W} = \frac{YCdc}{Y(Cdc/da) + C(dc/dc) + XCdc}$$

$$= \frac{Y}{(Y/da) + (1/dc) + X}$$

$$= Z$$

Knowing the values of X, Y, da and dc, Z can be determined. The bulk density of the coarse aggregate (K) is then measured and the percentage of sand required is

$$\frac{(Z - K)}{Z} 100$$

The following points should be noted:

(a) In assuming that coarse aggregate bulk is equal to that of our container, and that eqn. (1) is also true, we also assume that our sand is such that it can infiltrate between the packed coarse aggregate particles without pushing them apart; therefore, the largest sand particles should ideally be less in size than the smallest voids between the coarse aggregates.

(b) The sand, while obviously required to be finely graded, from point (a), must not be too fine otherwise the water demand is too high.

(c) The sand percentage must not be less than about 20% otherwise the mix is not practicable.

(d) Since there are volume changes in cement paste during early hydration, the assumption in (ii), above, is not true but is acceptable as the changes are very small.

As a good guide the following indicates the maximum sand particle sizes that can be reasonably used with relevant coarse aggregate sizes:

Coarse aggregate	Sand
37·5–20·0 mm	All passing a 2·36 mm sieve
20·0–10·0 mm	All passing a 1·18 mm sieve
10·0–5·0 mm	All passing a 600 μ sieve

6.2.2 Bulk density of the coarse aggregate

This can be measured fairly easily. It is advisable to use a container which is not less than about eight times the maximum particle size. The bulk density should be obtained from aggregate fed into a container under vibration so that the particles can pack properly into a close arrangement. About six samples should normally be taken for measurement in order to get a reasonable mean value; if the aggregate particle shape is more variable, more samples will have to be taken. A change in particle shape will affect the bulk density and hence the mortar demand of the mix, which can have obvious undesirable consequences.

6.2.3 Water/cement and aggregate/cement ratios

Water/cement ratio (X) is fixed from the usual considerations of strength and durability. From data given by Stewart,[4] relating water/aggregate ratio to aggregate/cement ratio, for constant workability—suitable for vibration—Tables 6.1 and 6.2 are obtained.

TABLE 6.1

Aggregate/cement ratio and water/cement ratio for river aggregate of different maximum sizes

	Aggregate/cement ratio (by weight)						Maximum aggregate size (mm)
	3	4	5	6	7	8	
Water/cement ratio (by weight)	0·32	0·36	0·39	0·42	0·46	0·50	37·5
	0·32	0·36	0·40	0·44	0·49	0·56	20·0
	0·37	0·42	0·47	0·52	0·59	0·67	10·0

The workability is intended to be very low but not necessarily to correspond exactly to that indicated by the compacting factor.

TABLE 6.2

Aggregate/cement ratio and water/cement ratio for crushed rock aggregate of different maximum sizes

	Aggregate/cement ratio (by weight)						Maximum aggregate size (mm)
	3	4	5	6	7	8	
Water/cement ratio (by weight)	0·34	0·38	0·41	0·46	0·52	0·58	37·5
	0·34	0·39	0·43	0·48	0·55	0·62	20·0
	0·40	0·47	0·54	0·61	0·69	0·77	10·0

6.2.4 Specific gravity of aggregates

da = the specific gravity of the combined aggregates.

Since the specific gravities of the fine and coarse aggregates are frequently different and since the percentage of sand in the aggregates cannot be computed until the value of *da* is known, a process of trial and error must be used. A sand percentage is assumed from experience and *da* computed on this basis. This is then used to work out the value of Z. From this, and knowing the bulk density of the coarse aggregate, we find the percent sand and if it tallies with our assumed percent we have been successful. If not then we start again, assuming a modified value.

Typical values of sand are:

Aggregate maximum size	Percent sand
37·5 mm	20–25
20·0 mm	25–30
10·0 mm	28–35

The values of specific gravity required are those based on saturated, surface-dry conditions of the aggregate.

6.2.5 Particle interference

It has already been pointed out that coarse aggregate of particular maximum size requires sand which is of a fineness such that it can enter the voids between the packed coarse aggregate particles, under vibration. If some of the sand cannot do this, the coarse aggregate particles tend to be pushed apart, jamming probably occurs and the result is that the void volume in the compacted aggregate is increased. Since the mortar content is computed on the basis of a smaller void volume, it will therefore be insufficient to satisfactorily fill the new void space. This mix will be unsatisfactory.

This increase in void volume can occur either (a) by having sand that is too coarse, or (b) by having a coarse aggregate that has too many particles passing the lower sieve size. A closely graded, single-size, coarse aggregate is best. A nominally single-sized 20·0 mm aggregate can have up to 20% passing the 10·0 mm sieve and 5% passing the 5·0 mm sieve and can satisfy the grading requirement of BS 882.(14) This will require considerably more sand, of a fixed grading, than, say, a 20·0 mm aggregate with 5% passing the 10 mm sieve.

Once the aggregate proportions have been tried and adjusted it is important that the grading of the aggregates should be closely controlled.

6.3 EXAMPLE OF MIX DESIGN

Aggregates are 20·0 mm maximum size gravel and a Zone 3 sand with the following gradings:

	Sieve size							
	20·0 mm	10·0 mm	5·0 mm	2·36 mm	1·18 mm	600 μ	300 μ	150 μ
Percent passing	100	5						
			100	100	100	75	30	5

The bulk density of the gravel = 1 440 kg/m^3.

Specific gravity of gravel = 2·55.

Specific gravity of sand = 2·65.

Let us assume that the water/cement ratio required is 0·50. From Table 6.1 we see the aggregate/cement ratio is about 7. Assume

30/70 fine/coarse aggregate ratio (noting that the 30% refers to compatible sand):

$$da = (0{\cdot}30 \times 2{\cdot}65) + (0{\cdot}70 \times 2{\cdot}55)$$
$$= 2{\cdot}58$$
$$Z = \frac{7{\cdot}0}{[(7{\cdot}0/2{\cdot}58) + (1/3{\cdot}15) + 0{\cdot}50)]\ 1000}$$
$$= 1{\cdot}99 \times 1\,000\ \text{kg/m}^3$$
$$\%\ \text{sand} = \left(\frac{1{\cdot}99 - 1{\cdot}44}{1{\cdot}99}\right) 100$$
$$= 27{\cdot}6\%,\ \text{say}\ 28\%$$

(This will give a value of $da = 2{\cdot}583$, so it is quite satisfactory.) Mix proportions are 1:1·96:5·04: 0·50.

6.4 THE SPECIFIC SURFACE METHOD

This method has been discussed in the previous chapter and it will be apparent that, in principle, it is, of course, applicable to gap-graded concrete also. It takes no account of particle interference and there must be a 'type' grading (*e.g.* those given in Fig. 4.6) which one is using as a standard of comparison. It will indicate the same sand content—for given aggregates and 'type' grading—irrespective of richness and workability of mix. But this can be allowed for by choosing the type grading to suit these requirements.

Using the gradings in Section 6.3 we see that if we want to approximate to the lower limit of the grading envelope shown in Fig. 4.6 we would require about 20% sand and to the upper limit about 27% sand. Since we know from experience that the former is a very low figure for a conventional mix as lean and dry as this, we would probably go for a sand content of about 30%.

6.5 SOME GENERAL COMMENTS

It is difficult to compare gap-graded and continuously-graded mixes; in fact, it is merely academic to try, since their objects are common to both, they produce concretes that have similar mechanical properties and from a given set of aggregates one would produce one type and not both types of gradings. In other words, perfectly good concrete can be produced from either and the availability of aggregates will generally be the deciding factor. With correctly designed mixes the characteristics of the aggregates are automatically accounted for.

There may be occasions when a gap-graded mix may be more desirable, *e.g.* in dealing with fine and coarse aggregates with widely different specific gravities, but normally it will be economics that indicate what is required. Gap-graded concretes, with low mortar contents, are very sensitive to water content changes and control must be very good otherwise badly segregated concrete will result. On the other hand, because of the coarse aggregate content and packing arrangement, density changes are minimised in the freshly compacted concrete.

The method suggested by Stewart is interesting in that it is an attempt to rationalise the relationships between water, cement and aggregate contents and to get away from 'type' gradings which may be impossible to reproduce. It is, of course, an approximate method and does not displace the art of finalising mix proportions. They are more critical here than normally, as the mortar content is low and may have to be increased to allow for loss in the mixer, dumper, skip, and so on to cope with the higher mortar demand of some previously mentioned situations (*see* Section 4.6). Trial mixes are rather more of a problem than with conventional continuously-graded concrete; the workability is intended to be very low and this, combined with the rather unusual appearance of the fresh concrete—lacking fines and having a predominance of larger particles—may cause extra water to be added to 'improve' it. This is about the worst thing that can be done. The concrete usually compacts very well under vibration but, of course, the efficiency of the compacting equipment in the laboratory may be well below that available on site; the difference between a small vibrating table and, say, a 50 mm or 75 mm poker vibrator can be very marked! Because the trial mix batch may be very small, the loss of even a little mortar in, for example, coating the mixer pan, or the trowels, or the surfaces of cube moulds, may be serious and lead to great difficulty in finishing the surface of the compacted concrete. Some allowance (perhaps an extra 5%) must be made for this; with experience it is readily possible to relate trial mix performance to the full-scale site potential.

Chapter 7

MIX DESIGN FOR HIGH STRENGTH CONCRETE

7.1 INTRODUCTION

High strength concrete is not fundamentally different from normal strength concrete; it is different only in its level of strength and associated properties and in their ramifications. Being usually rich and/or of very low workability this concrete exhibits behaviour which is evident in these relatively exaggerated regions but which is not clearly defined in normal regions of cement content and workability.

It is interesting to consider, as a very elementary approach to the nominal compressive strength, the three elements of the concrete, namely, paste, aggregate and paste–aggregate bond. In high strength concrete the paste is, of course, of high strength (about 100 to 120 N/mm^2); hard, strong aggregates are used with crushing strength of perhaps 200 to 250 N/mm^2 and higher; therefore failure in the concrete seems likely to be initiated at the aggregate/paste interface, a likelihood that is increased by the presence there of microcracks and by the large difference between the stiffnesses of the paste and aggregate. In other words, the strength of this concrete may well be dependent upon the bond strength of paste to aggregate.

If this is so then it is perhaps to be expected that those aggregates which are much stronger than the paste and which possess roughened and/or reactive surfaces giving very good paste bond, should result in strengths higher than similar concretes made with smoother or less reactive aggregates. This may partly explain the effect of using crushed granite and limestones instead of flint gravels.

In this chapter, high strength concrete refers to concrete obtained through using ordinary or rapid hardening Portland cements cured at normal temperatures.

7.2 DESCRIPTION OF DATA

The data available is from a paper by Erntroy and Shacklock[26] and refers specifically to the materials used in that work. The principles are the same for other materials, but the numerical values associated with them—strength, workability, and so on—may be quite different, hence the importance of trial mixes.

Some important data on the materials used are given in Tables 7.1, 7.2 and 7.3.

TABLE 7.1

Some characteristics of the cements used

Property		Ordinary Portland	Rapid-hardening Portland
Specific surface		3 375 cm²/g	4 275 cm²/g
Water/cement ratio for cement paste of standard consistency		0·24	0·308
Compressive strength of standard vibrated mortar cubes (N/mm²)	1 day	9·0	15·5
	3 days	24·5	33·5
	7 days	35·0	44·5
	28 days	47·0	53·5
	91 days	52·5	63·0

These data may help with the interpretation of the concrete test results on which the mix design is based and may be useful in dealing with cements of different characteristics.

The aggregates used were a natural Thames Valley pit sand combined with either a natural Thames Valley gravel or crushed Leicestershire granite. Some information available indicates that

TABLE 7.2

Some properties of the aggregates used

Property		Irregular gravel 20·0 mm	Irregular gravel 10·0 mm	Crushed granite 20·0 mm	Crushed granite 10·0 mm	Natural sand
Absorption (%)	after 5 min	1·3	3·0	0·3	0·6	1·5
	after 24 h	1·9	3·7	0·4	0·7	1·8
Apparent specific gravity after 5 min absorption		2·54	2·55	2·65	2·65	2·63

other crushed rocks and natural gravels are reasonably comparable with these.

The grading of the aggregates was maintained constant over the range of aggregate/cement ratios used (*i.e.* from 2·5:1 to 5·5:1 by weight). This grading, for each maximum size, is shown below in Table 7.3.

TABLE 7.3

Gradings used for 20·0 *mm and* 10·0 *mm aggregates*

Aggregate maximum size (mm)	BS sieve size (mm or micron) 20·0	10·0	5·0	2·36	1·18	600	300	150
	Percent, by weight, passing							
20·0	100	45	30	23	16	9	2	0
10·0		100	30	20	16	12	4	0

Thus grading is not at all critical, particularly in the rich mixes, and departures from it will not be serious. It approximates to about 30% of a Zone 2 sand and varying that from, say, 25% to 35% over the range of aggregate/cement ratios will be acceptable.

7.3 SOME IMPORTANT POINTS

The following illustrate certain phenomena which underly all concrete data but which have sufficiently measurable dimensions to be worthy of note in the higher strength levels, *i.e.* above, say, 40 to 50 N/mm^2. The actual numerical values, of course, apply only to the specific materials used to derive the data.

(1) The fineness of the cement had a marked effect on the compacting factor. In general, with mixes of equal aggregate/cement ratio the rapid-hardening Portland cement mixes needed an increase of 0·03 in the water/cement ratios to maintain the same compacting factor as the ordinary Portland cement mix. This is presumably related to the relative fineness of the two cements and their water/cement ratios for pastes of standard consistency.

(2) For a given total water/cement ratio the crushed granite mixes gave higher compressive strength than the natural gravel mixes, the difference becoming less marked until at the higher water/cement ratios there was little difference between them.

(3) For mixes of comparable workability and aggregate/cement ratio it was found that the granite mixes had higher compressive strength than the gravel mixes, the difference becoming more marked as the strength increased.

(4) For a given water/cement ratio, as the workability decreased the compressive strength increased; for example, a 3·5:1 aggregate/cement ratio might have a strength of 50 N/mm^2 at a particular age and a 5·5:1 aggregate/cement ratio 60 N/mm^2 at the same age and water/cement ratio. In other words, leaner mixes had higher compressive strengths than richer mixes of the same water/cement ratio. The benefit gained through using a leaner mix must, of course, be offset against the lower workability and the consequently greater expense in handling and compacting the concrete. In general, there will be practical limitations placed on the leanness of the mix consistent with the compacting and other equipment available.

(5) The strength of very rich, very dry mixes was virtually independent of the richness; at higher workabilities a change in aggregate/cement ratio, at constant compacting factor, caused a marked change in strength (*see* Table 7.4).

TABLE 7.4

Typical relationship between compressive strength and aggregate/cement ratio for various compacting factors

Compacting factor	Aggregate/cement ratio by weight			
	2·5	3·0	3·5	4·0
	Compressive strength (N/mm^2)			
0·68	54·0	53·0	52·5	52·0
0·78	48·0	45·5	43·5	41·5
0·92	39·0	35·0	31·0	28·0

It may therefore be worthwhile to try to use very low workability to get the required strength rather than use higher workability requiring very rich mixes.

7.4 MIX DESIGN

Since using very wet mixes of high workability is unlikely and inadvisable for high strength concrete, this level has been dropped and a further level added which is 'extremely low' workability. This corresponds to a compacting factor of about 0·68 and applies to concrete placed in sections subject to intensive vibration and/or pressure. It supplements the values given in Table 4.2 (Section 4.4).

We have seen that the compressive strength depends on water/cement ratio, aggregate type, cement type and workability or richness of mix. The workability depends upon type of cement, type and size of aggregate and water content. From these inter-relations we can use the available data to design our mixes.

7.4.1 Procedure

Basically the procedure is thus:

(1) Strength and workability are chosen as usual.

(2) For a given type of cement and aggregate there is a relation between strength, water/cement ratio, workability and age. The strength, workability and age are fixed and so we can select the water/cement ratio, correspondingly, for the particular cement and aggregate.

(3) For a given type of cement and aggregate there is a relation between compacting factor, water/cement ratio and aggregate/cement ratio. We can therefore choose the aggregate/cement ratio accordingly.

Let us take point (2) above, and see what this involves. We have two types of cement—ordinary and rapid-hardening Portland. We have two types of aggregate—irregular gravel and sand, and crushed granite and sand. Each type of cement can be combined with each set of aggregates which gives four relations. For each relation we have various ages of test from, say, one day to three months and for any one age we have curves relating strength to water/cement ratio for four degrees of workability. Therefore, we have four times as many relationships as ages of concrete, each relationship being of the form strength versus water/cement ratio for 'extremely low', 'very low', 'low' and 'medium' degrees of workability. Figure 7.1 shows a typical example.

As far as point (3) is concerned, the position is not complicated by the age of concrete but we have two maximum sizes of aggregate for each type of aggregate and each type of cement. This gives us eight relations, each one consisting of compacting factor versus

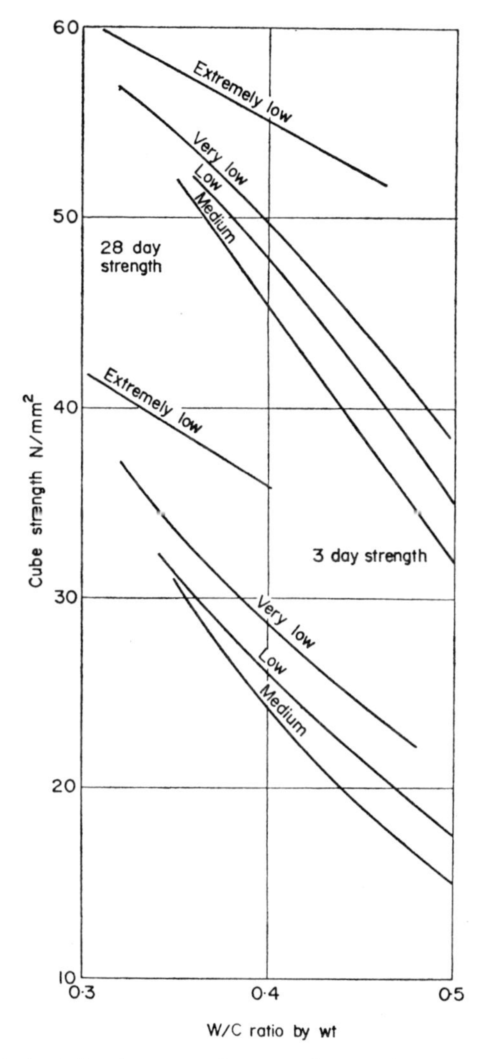

FIG. 7.1 Typical relation between cube strength, water/cement ratio and workability for two ages, one type of cement and one type of coarse aggregate.

water/cement ratio for different aggregate/cement ratios. Figure 7.2 shows a typical example.

Figures 7.3, 7.4 and 7.5 give the necessary data for choosing the aggregate/cement ratio.

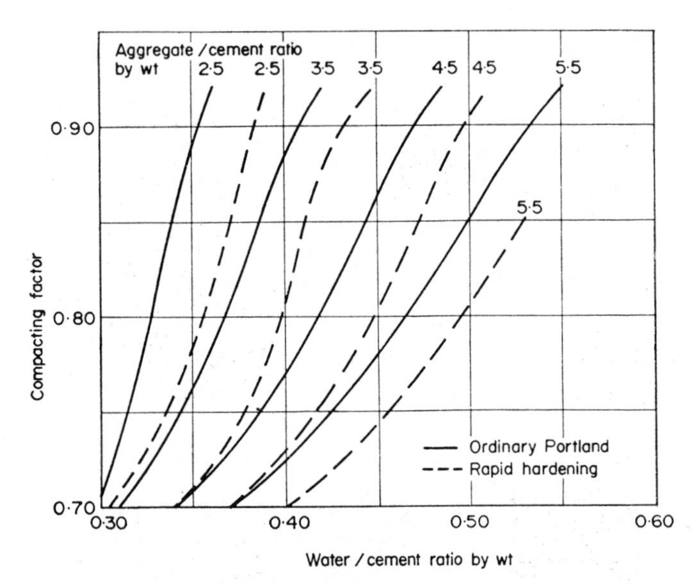

FIG. 7.2 Typical relation between compacting factor, water/cement ratio and aggregate/cement ratio (by weight), for two types of cement and aggregate of one type and maximum size.

The following examples will illustrate the use of the data:

Example 1

Concrete is required for a pretensioned roof purlin which is 150 mm × 100 mm in section with stressing wires at close centres restricting the aggregate maximum size to 10·0 mm. The characteristic 3-day compressive strength required is 28 N/mm^2. Intensive vibration (and pressure, if required) can be used for compacting the concrete and supervision is good. Experience has shown that the margin between design mean strength and characteristic strength should be about 10 N/mm^2 for these circumstances. Therefore, design strength = 38 N/mm^2. Workability is extremely low.

Using Figs. 7.3, 7.4 and 7.5 we get the data shown in Table 7.5.

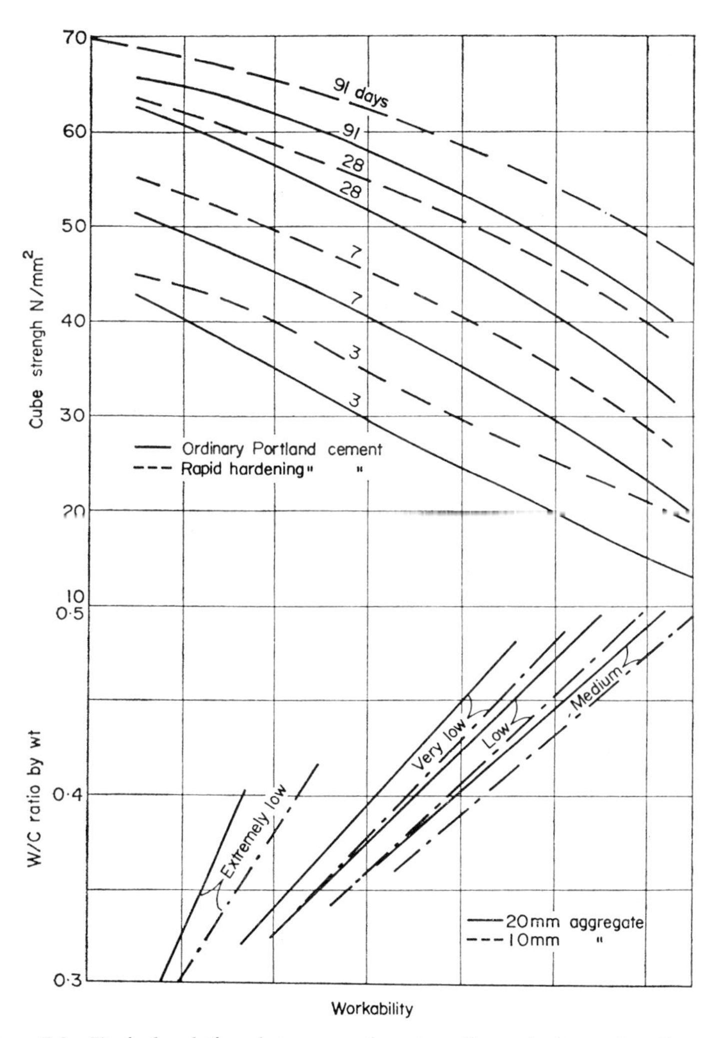

FIG. 7.3 Typical relation between cube strength, water/cement ratio and workability for different ages using Portland cement and two sizes of gravel coarse aggregate (based on Ref. 26).

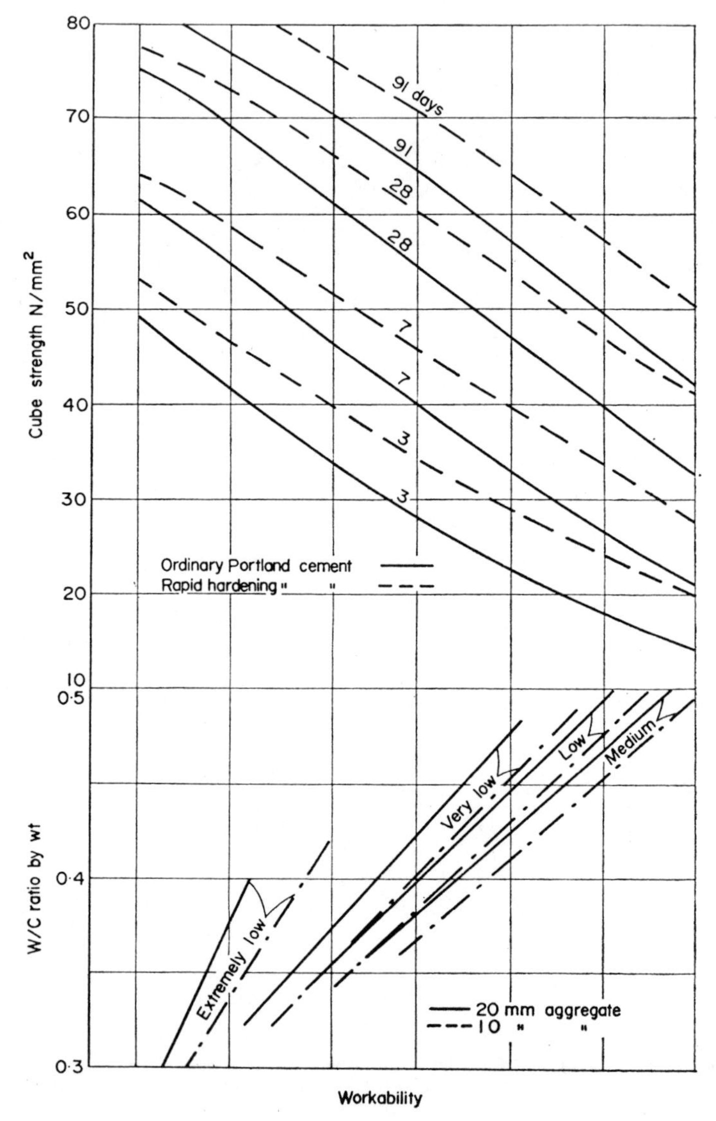

Fig. 7.4 Typical relation between cube strength, water/cement ratio and workability for different ages using Portland cement and two sizes of granite coarse aggregate (based on Ref. 26).

TABLE 7.5

Type of cement	Type of aggregate	Water/cement ratio	Aggregate/cement ratio
Ordinary Portland	gravel	0·33	3·5
	granite	0·38	5·2
Rapid-hardening	gravel	0·40	4·9
	granite	—	—

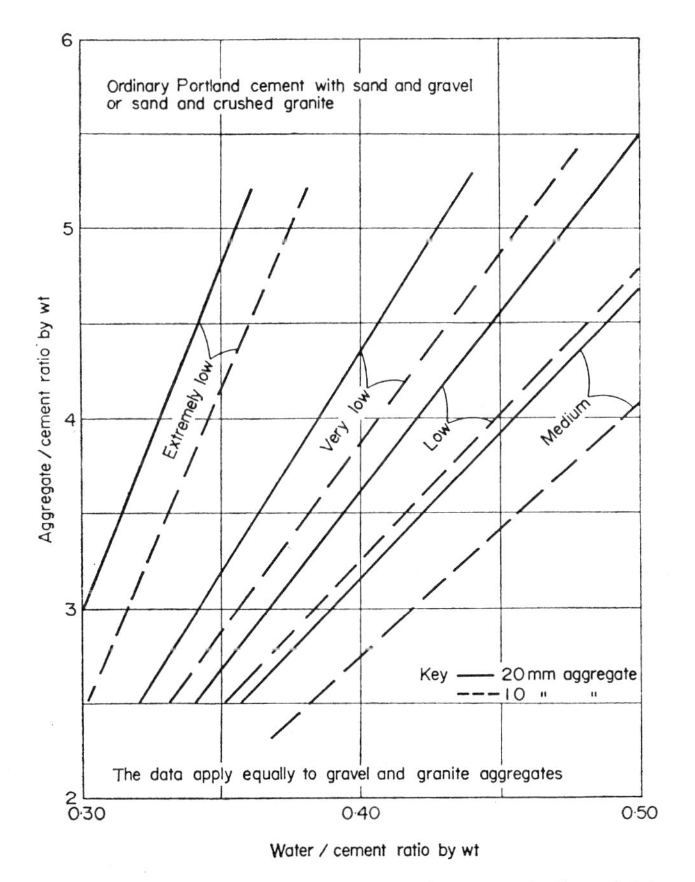

FIG. 7.5(a) Typical relation between aggregate/cement ratio (by weight), water/cement ratio and workability for ordinary Portland cement with aggregates of two types and two maximum sizes.

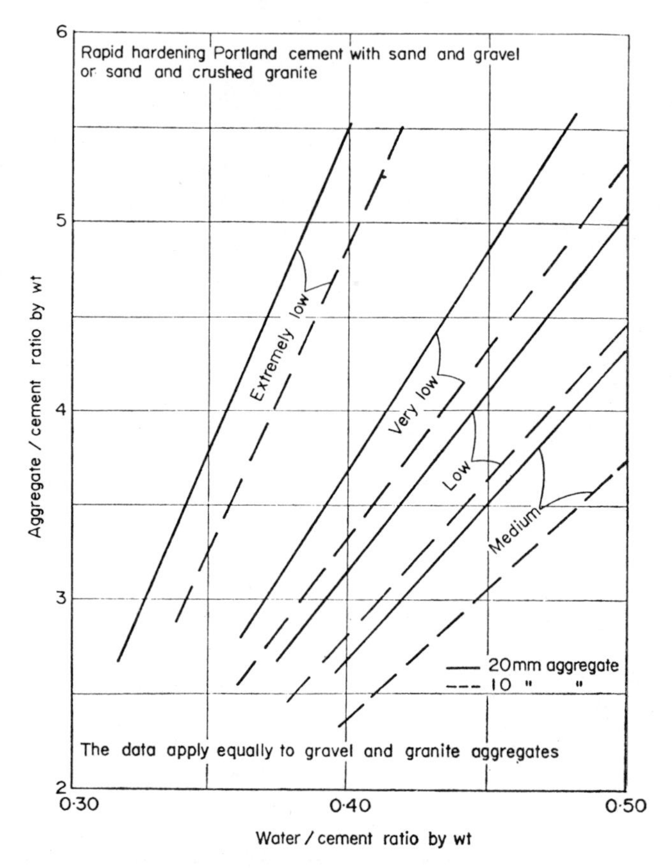

FIG. 7.5(b) Typical relation between aggregate/cement ratio (by weight), water/cement ratio and workability for rapid hardening Portland cement with aggregates of two types and two maximum sizes.

For these particular conditions we might therefore use a 5·2:1 mix with about 30% sand, depending upon the relative materials' costs. We find, using a combination of crushed granite and rapid-hardening Portland cement, that the data in Fig. 7.4 does not cover 'extremely low' workability and 38 N/mm^2 strength at 3 days. We therefore cannot use this particular set of factors. (We might, of course, extrapolate and use a water/cement ratio of 0·42, with a 5·5:1 mix as an estimate for a trial mix, giving us a strength of about 40 N/mm^2 at 3 days.)

Example 2
Concrete is required to have a design mean strength at 28 days of 55 N/mm². Very low workability is suitable and 20·0 mm maximum size aggregate with a Zone 2 natural sand is to be used. Table 7.6 shows the relevant water/cement and aggregate/cement ratios.

TABLE 7.6

Type of cement	Type of aggregate	Water/cement ratio	Aggregate/cement ratio
Ordinary Portland	gravel	0·36	3·5
	granite	0·42	4·9
Rapid-hardening	gravel	0·40	3·7
	granite	0·48	5·5

From the choice of four mixes the one that is most economical is chosen; the relative costs of granite against gravel, of cement against aggregate and of ordinary Portland against rapid hardening cement will be taken into account to obtain the most acceptable combination assuming a cement content compatible with durability requirements.

7.5 SUMMARY

'High strength' concrete does not become evident by a sudden change in the behaviour of 'ordinary strength' concrete. There is a gradual effect that becomes more noticeable when the strength level exceeds about 40 to 45 N/mm². There naturally cannot be a precise level of strength which defines this change in effect. The effects are on strength and workability, requiring us to take into account in our mix proportioning the ramifications of fineness of cement on workability and of type of aggregate and aggregate/cement ratio on strength. Data available, relating to specific materials, enable us, in principle, to do this. It is essential to supplement these data by trial mixes using the particular materials intended for the concrete.

Perhaps the most important thing to be learnt from this procedure is that selection of materials (both cement and aggregates) becomes more critical as the concrete strength increases and that if very high strengths are required (75 to 80 N/mm² and higher) relatively few materials may be suitable. The process of selection of mix proportions described here illustrates very well the important parameters that *always* need examination and which the careful concrete technologist never forgets but which, for normal concrete, are conveniently reduced in a kind of blurred 'blanket treatment' of the mix design approach. High standard concrete is a confirmation of the truism that no two concretes are the same.

Chapter 8

MIX DESIGN FOR AIR-ENTRAINED CONCRETE

8.1 WHAT IS IT?

Air-entrained concrete is concrete containing air in a rather special form and of a controlled volume. It is to be distinguished from concrete with 'entrapped' air, *i.e.* air due to undercompaction. The latter is usually in the form of irregular voids, generally fairly large, non-uniformly distributed throughout the concrete and of uncontrolled volume. The former is in the form of regular, almost spherical voids ranging in size from about 0·02 mm to 0·2 mm diameter and is distributed uniformly throughout the mortar in the concrete.

8.2 HOW IS IT OBTAINED?

Various agents are used to entrain air, *e.g.* natural wood resins, some animal and vegetable fats and oils, wetting agents, etc. Some are in powder form and others in liquid form, the latter being more common. It is very important that the agent used should cause air to be entrained not only in the correct volume but also of the correct type, *i.e.* as a very large number of small bubbles rather than as a smaller number of large bubbles. The latter are unstable under vibration and of little benefit to the concrete. Most reputable agents satisfy these requirements. The quantity of agent required is usually of the order of 0·10 to 0·20% by weight of the cement and should be added with the mixing water to get uniform dispersion in the concrete.

There are various dispensers available which allow a pre-set amount to be discharged into the mixer either automatically or semi-automatically. If very concentrated agents are used, or small batches of concrete mixed, it is advisable to incorporate the agent as a dilute solution, the volume of which can be more readily controlled accurately.

8.3 WHY IS IT REQUIRED?

In the UK air-entrained concrete is used largely in roads, airfield runways and ancillary highway structures, such as bridge parapets; frost resistance and resistance to the more severe effects of de-icing salt are the main reasons for the inclusion of the air.

It has been known for many years that concrete containing entrained air is more frost resistant than concrete without it, although the exact mechanism of failure was not fully understood. It is assumed that as freezing occurs and water is driven through the paste by the expansion on freezing, the proximity of air bubbles prevents generation of dangerous hydraulic pressures which would otherwise be set up. Because of the pore structure, the paste is never saturated and there is always accommodation for water migrating under pressure. If the water has too far to migrate—through capillaries in the paste—pressure may become excessive and it is for this reason that a large number of small bubbles of air is required to ensure that the average bubble spacing is not greater than about 0·2 mm.

8.4 EFFECTS ON PROPERTIES OF CONCRETE

8.4.1 Strength

For practical purposes it is usually assumed that strength is affected in the same way as it is by entrapped air, *i.e.* every 1% of entrained air causes a drop of about 5% in the compressive strength. This is more for rich and less for lean mixes and may be of the order of 3 to 4% for cement contents of 250 kg/m^2 and 9 to 10% for 400 kg/m^3. The effects are very much related to the agent and cement used, as well as to the cement content, workability, and so on.

8.4.2 Workability

This is increased by entrained air and Wright[27] found that the compacting factor increased by about 0·07 for every 5% air. The increase tends to be greater for lean than for rich mixes, for wet than for dry mixes and for angular aggregate than for rounded aggregate mixes. The 'V–B' test also reflects similar consequences of entraining air, the effect being, approximately, to reduce by half the 'V–B' time.[28] If constant workability is required, *i.e.* relative to a comparable, non-air-entrained mix, the water content can, of course, be reduced.

8.4.3 Modified pore structure

This favourably affects the frost resistance, the permeability and absorption and the stability of the concrete. The first of these is the property which is most important, the others being fairly marginal, except the increased stability which is often a most useful side-effect.

8.5 FACTORS AFFECTING THE QUANTITY OF AIR ENTRAINED

These can be summarised as follows:

(1) type and amount of admixture;
(2) workability of the mix;
(3) mix proportions;
(4) type and grading of aggregate;
(5) characteristics of the cement;
(6) mixing time and mixer type;
(7) temperature.

(1) There are many admixtures available and the manufacturers' data is best used as a *guide* for preliminary mixes.

(2) The more workable the concrete the less admixture tends to be required to entrain a given quantity of air. Some typical experimental results illustrate this:

Cement content (kg/m^3)	Workability	Agent (percent by weight of cement)	Air content (percent by volume)
300	low	0·11	5
300	high	0·09	5½

In practice, particularly until some experience with air-entrained concrete has been obtained, this may make control slightly more difficult than usual as this interdependence of workability, air content and quantity of agent may require some careful choice of water and agent contents to maintain constant workability and air volume. A change in workability will probably mean a change in air entrained without a change in agent quantity. With some experience this situation can be adequately coped with.

(3) Richer mixes generally require more agent than leaner mixes for the same amount of air. The following experimental data indicate some typical values:

Cement content (kg/m^3)	Workability	Agent (percent by weight of cement)	Air content (percent by volume)
385	high	0·09	5½
300	high	0·08	6½

The cement tends to inhibit the formation of air, the effects being influenced by chemical composition; rich mixes are unlikely to benefit much from entrained air.

(4) Angular aggregates may entrain more air than rounded aggregates for given conditions, but the effect is fairly small. There are conflicting data on the effects of grading and it may be assumed to be of secondary importance. Very fine aggregate—passing a 75 micron sieve—has an inhibiting effect.

(5) Finely ground cements entrain less air than the more coarsely ground ones.

(6) With stable agents the length of mixing time is not normally critical so long as the minimum time is about one minute; if less than this the amount of air may well depend upon length of mixing time. If the air content increases with increasing mixing time this probably indicates that the agent is not suitable.

(7) The higher the concrete temperature the lower the amount of air entrained for otherwise equal conditions, but this is usually unimportant and for large temperature changes is readily counteracted by changing the agent dosage.

8.6 MEASURING THE AIR CONTENT

Three methods are used for this purpose but the most satisfactory, for normal, dense aggregates, is the pressure method. This entails applying a known pressure to a known volume of concrete (containing air) and measuring the decrease in volume; the latter is related to the air content and is registered on a calibrated glass water gauge as percent air, by volume of the concrete. The standard method of test is given in BS 1881.[5] The result obtained from this test includes entrapped air and therefore the entrained air can be taken as about 1 to 1½% less than this. It should be noted that it is the air content of the *mortar* that is of more importance, but it is the *concrete* that is usually tested and the result obtained is expressed in terms of the volume of the latter. This naturally affects comparisons between mixes of different mortar contents.

8.7 MIX DESIGN

Wright[27] suggested a method of mix design which has been criticised as being too cumbersome, apparently 'exact' and not a very practical approach. Whether, as a matter of practice, one would choose to use it or not it is worth examining because it gives a step-by-step account of logically modifying a non-air-entrained mix into a comparable air-entrained mix.

This approach is very useful in helping one to visualise the mechanics of modification.

8.7.1 Wright's method

The following are the steps involved:

(1) Determine the mix proportions using the Road Note No. 4 approach (this means getting the mix right in fact and not just on paper).

(2) Convert weight proportions to absolute volume proportions (divide by specific gravities; approximate values are acceptable here).

(3) Express these volumes as percentages of the total.

(4) The aggregate volume is reduced by an amount equal to the entrained air but the overall volume is kept constant to maintain constant cement content. It is unwise to replace only sand with air as this leads to harshness. The reduction in aggregate volume is divided between fine and coarse fractions in accordance with stability requirements and usually means that the coarse aggregate is decreased by 1 to 2%.

(5) Air improves workability so reduce water to maintain fixed workability. For every 1% air added, *W*% water is subtracted, the value of *W* being obtained from data given by Wright (*see* Table 8.1).

Make up the volume of water subtracted by adding an equal volume of aggregate in the same proportion as in the original mix.

(6) Convert these absolute volume figures to weight percentages.

(7) Finally convert to weight proportions.

TABLE 8.1

Values of W (percent water/one percent air) for aggregates of 20·0 mm maximum size (after Wright)

Aggregate/cement ratio by weight	Aggregate particle shape		
	Rounded	Irregular	Angular
6:1	0·325	0·375	0·425
7·5:1	0·40	0·45	0·50
9:1	0·45	0·50	0·55

The following example illustrates the procedure, using a mix designed as in Road Note No. 4, the aggregates used being a sand and gravel of irregular particle shape and 20·0 mm maximum size:

	Cement	Sand	Gravel	Water	Air	Total
(1) Proportions by weight	1	2	4	0·55	0	
(2) Absolute volumes	1/3·12	2/2·55	4/2·50	0·55		
	0·32	0·79	1·60	0·55	0	3·26
(3) % absolute volume	9·80	24·10	49·00	17·10		100·00
(4) Add air, subtract aggregate	—	4·00	1·00	—	5	100·00
	9·80	20·10	48·00	17·10	5	
(5) Subtract water and add aggregate	—	0·60	1·30	1·90	—	
	9·80	20·70	49·30	15·20	5	
(6) Convert to weights	31	53	123	15·20		
(7) Proportions	1	1·71	3·97	0·49		

The specific gravities of cement, sand and gravel are taken as 3·12, 2·55 and 2·50 respectively.

W taken as 0·375 from Table 8.1. 5 × 0·375 = 1·875, say 1·9, and this is split into 0·60 and 1·30.

Final mix 1:5·70, water/cement ratio 0·49, with 30% sand + 5% air.

8.7.2 Estimated strength

Original mix water/cement ratio 0·55—28-day strength about 38 N/mm^2

modified mix water/cement ratio 0·49—28-day strength 43 N/mm^2

$$\text{reduction in strength} = 5 \times \frac{5{\cdot}5}{100} \times 43 \simeq 12\ \text{N/mm}^2$$

$$\text{modified strength} = 43 - 12\ \text{N/mm}^2$$

$$= 31\ \text{N/mm}^2$$

If necessary, redesign mix for (38 + 7) N/mm^2, *i.e.* 45 N/mm^2, to maintain the 38 N/mm^2 required.

8.7.3 Absolute volume method

One other way to design the mix is to modify one, already designed in accordance with Road Note No. 4, in the following manner:

(1) Reduce sand by about $\frac{3}{4}$ to 1% for every 1% air. The final choice will depend upon the mix requirements.

(2) Reduce water content by about 4·5 to 5·0 kg/m^3 for every 1% air.

(3) Maintain the same cement content.

This results in new water/cement and aggregate/cement ratios.

Taking our previous example of 1:2:4, water/cement ratio 0·55, we compute the cement content assuming full compaction of the concrete:

$$\text{cement content} = \frac{1\,000}{(1/3{\cdot}12) + (2/2{\cdot}55) + (4/2{\cdot}50) + 0{\cdot}55}$$

$$= 305\ \text{kg/m}^3$$

Therefore

$$\text{gravel} = 305 \times 4 = 1\,220\ \text{kg/m}^3$$

$$\text{sand} = 305 \times 2 = 610\ \text{kg/m}^3$$

$$\text{water} = 305 \times 0{\cdot}55 = 168\ \text{kg/m}^3$$

Reduce water content by, say, 23·5 kg/m^3 (*i.e.* 4·7 × 5·0). Therefore new water content is 168 − 23·5 ≃ 145 kg/m^3. Reduce sand content by, say, 4%, *i.e.* to 29%. Keep cement content constant at 305 kg/m^3. New nominal water/cement ratio is 145/305 = 0·48.

The ingredients of the air-entrained mix are:

$$\begin{aligned} \text{cement content} &= 305\ \text{kg/m}^3 = 98\ \text{l absolute volume} \\ \text{water content} &= 145\ \text{kg/m}^3 = 145\ \text{l absolute volume} \\ \text{air} &= 5\% = 50\ \text{l absolute volume} \\ \text{total} &= 293\ \text{l absolute volume} \end{aligned}$$

Therefore

$$\begin{aligned} \text{aggregate content} &= 1\,000 - 293 \\ &= 707\ \text{l absolute volume} \\ \text{sand } 29\% \times 707 &= 205\ \text{l absolute volume} \\ \text{gravel } 71\% \times 707 &= 502\ \text{l absolute volume} \end{aligned}$$

The weights (kg) per cubic metre of concrete are:

$$\begin{aligned} \text{cement} &= 305 \\ \text{sand } (205 \times 2{\cdot}55) &= 522 \\ \text{gravel } (502 \times 2{\cdot}50) &= 1\,260 \\ \text{water} &= 145 \end{aligned}$$

The proportions, by weight, are 1:1·71:4·13:0·48, *i.e.* aggregate/cement ratio about 5·8, water/cement ratio 0·48, which is virtually identical with the mix in the previous example.

It may be noted that in computing the absolute volumes of sand and gravel, the percentages by weight were used; these should strictly have been percentages by absolute volume, but unless there is a fairly large difference between the density of sand and gravel the effect is negligible.

8.8 CONCLUSION

The approach to mix design of air-entrained concrete is even more empirical than that of normal and high strength mixes because of the inclusion of the bubble-forming agent, the presence of which considerably influences the behaviour of the fresh and hardened concrete, but not exactly predictably. However, with practice and experience the choice of final mix proportions is really not difficult, especially once the behaviour of the agent has been observed. To begin with, certainly, it is probably easier to visualise the process if a correctly proportioned, non-air-entrained mix is modified to obtain the necessary air-entrained proportions; it will also help with the understanding of the changes likely to be necessary in the latter, arising out of the first trial mixes. And, of course, trial mixes, and adjustments thereof, will almost certainly be absolutely necessary.

Chapter 9

LIGHTWEIGHT AGGREGATE CONCRETE

9.1 BACKGROUND

To avoid misunderstandings a brief description of lightweight concrete is desirable because it is important that lightweight *aggregate* concrete be discussed without ambiguity.

Concrete is lightened by the introduction of air as: (a) air bubbles of rather coarse size (say, 1–3 mm diameter) in the mortar, from which coarse aggregate is usually excluded; this is known as aerated mortar or concrete and is not to be confused with air-entrained mortar or concrete; (b) air voids between coarse aggregate particles in a skeletal structure consisting of single-sized coarse aggregate bonded at contact points by a film of cement paste; this is 'no-fines' concrete; (c) air voids in the aggregate particles themselves, forming a 'no-fines' system or otherwise a normal, compacted concrete system; these are lightweight aggregates and are used in ways entirely similar to normal aggregates in concrete. This chapter is concerned with fully compacted, structural concrete made with lightweight aggregates; in many ways it is similar to normal concrete but the aggregates are of much higher porosity and lower density.

9.2 SOME REASONS FOR USAGE

The more important reasons for using this material are usually associated with the reduced density. Lower density of concrete is reflected in a lighter building superstructure which may require a considerably cheaper foundation. The density normally ranges from about 1 600 to 1 800 kg/m^3 as compared to about 2 400 kg/m^3 for normal concrete and hence tall or long-span structures, which have a high dead load component, are likely to benefit most.

Allied to reduced density is increased thermal insulation. The thermal conductivity of structural lightweight aggregate concrete is about half that of normal concrete with similar strength characteristics. With increased heating costs and more general awareness of the comforts of, and growing demands for, central heating, this becomes an important factor.

With the growth of prefabrication and improved erection and handling techniques, larger units are often desirable; obviously transport and on-site cranage can be more economically used with lower density concrete; if a structure is designed with lightweight aggregate concrete in mind, significant savings can be effected through cheaper unit cost of transport and/or lower capacity of cranes or larger units for a given handling capacity.

Despite being significantly more expensive in materials' cost, there can be a sizeable overall saving if advantage is taken of the above factors and, indeed, in some cases this material may be the only one possible.

9.3 LIGHTWEIGHT AGGREGATES

For structural concrete a number of lightweight aggregates are available in the UK; these are made from expanded clay, expanded slate, sintered pulverised fuel ash and foamed slag. Other materials are also obtainable (*e.g.* expanded Perlite, clinker and pumice) but they are not used for the production of structural concrete of the type considered here. The proprietary names of the former aggregates are:

Aggregate type	Proprietary name
Expanded clay	Lcca
Expanded clay	Aglite
Expanded slate	Solite
Sintered, pulverised fuel ash	Lytag
Foamed slag	Foamed slag

9.4 SOME PROPERTIES OF THE AGGREGATES

The most notable property of all the aggregates is their porosity which affects many other parameters. It may range from about 25 to

70% of the aggregate volume for a range of different types, and is, of course, dependent upon the particular raw material used, the processing adopted and the particle size of the finished material. It means, therefore, that each aggregate should be tested to establish numerical values of the different parameters and to assess the likely variations about the average values. For background information some data are given here (*see* Table 9.1) to indicate the approximate magnitude of values likely to be encountered.

9.4.1 Bulk density

The dry, loose bulk density ranges from about 380 to 870 kg/m^3 for coarse aggregates and 700 to 1 200 kg/m^3 for fine aggregates. For typical normal aggregates the corresponding figures are about 1 400 kg/m^3 and 1 600 kg/m^3.

9.4.2 Water absorption

The water absorption is, of course, time-dependent and very much depends upon the aggregate type and to some extent upon particle size. It varies from being fairly slow, continuing at a more or less constant rate for a long time, to being extremely rapid initially followed by a much slower constant rate for a long time. For many purposes the early absorption is the important one and this ranges from about 5 to 15% of the dry weight after 24 h, perhaps 3 to 12% after 30 min. Typical data for normal aggregates are 0·5 to 2% for 24 h absorption.

9.4.3 Specific gravity

Because of difficulties in determining the saturated surface–dry condition of many lightweight aggregates (a factor which obviously also affects the precision of water absorption data), data on specific gravity are not easily determined but, nevertheless, some guidance is possible.

The lightest coarse aggregate has a specific gravity, on a dry basis, of about 0·50 to 0·60, the others ranging from about 1·20 to 1·50. The fines are about 1·30 to 1·70, but depend very much upon grading, the density increasing with decrease in particle size, with the material passing a 150 μ sieve being about 2·20 to 2·50.

Comparable data for normal aggregates are in the range of about 2·50 to 2·70.

9.5 PROPERTIES OF FRESH CONCRETE

Although we can think of workability of lightweight aggregate concrete in the same way as we can of normal concrete, the actual numerical values of each may not be directly comparable. The same tests may be used for measuring relative workability but we must carefully interpret the results. The slump test is more limited in use than with normal aggregates and gives results lower than expected from a given workability. It is possible to have very workable concrete with very little or no slump; an increase in slump for these conditions would probably lead to an unstable mix with much bleeding. The corresponding slump with normal aggregates could probably be about 50 mm with quite a stable concrete resulting.

The compacting factor test was intended for use with normal aggregates and not with lightweight aggregates but, nevertheless, it is useful as a guide to relative workability. With the richer mixes, of course, it is found that the concrete will not flow through the hoppers in the apparatus but even so it is still of use. The value of compacting factor does not compare directly with the corresponding value in a sand and gravel concrete of the same observed workability. Nor is the relation the same for different lightweight aggregates; the richness of the mix also affects it. However, generalising, we can say that the compacting factor should normally be between about 0·75 and 0·85 for reasonable workability. With rich mixes it is possible to extend the range and with leaner mixes it may be more restricted; the range is also affected by the type of aggregate used.

The 'V–B' test is also applicable to these concretes and the values obtained are approximately 10 to 20 sec for compacting factor 0·75 (depending upon the aggregate used) and 5 to 12 sec for compacting factor 0·85.

In general, these lightweight aggregate concretes are more sensitive to changes in water content than natural aggregate concretes and a little excess water may cause a marked change in the stability of the mix. This is most evident in lean mixes and in those incorporating crushed coarse and fine aggregates.

The inclusion of entrained air or the replacement of the lightweight fines wholly or partly by natural sand generally improves the fresh concrete and alters the values of parameters given above. The changes depend upon the particular aggregate used and upon the quantity of air or sand incorporated.

9.6 PROPERTIES OF THE HARDENED CONCRETE

In general, it can be said that the behaviour of hardened lightweight aggregate concrete can be viewed in a way similar to that of normal concrete, *i.e.* the same properties and behavioural aspects are considered for both, although quantitatively there are significant differences. It is not intended here to do more than sketch in some outlines so that a few important points are not overlooked while concentrating on compressive strength.

9.6.1 Compressive strength

The compressive strength is very much affected by the same factors as it is in normal concrete, although the role of the aggregate is not quite the same because there is greater compatibility, with respect to deformation behaviour, between the aggregate and mortar; this means that, despite the rather weak aggregate particles, it is still readily possible to obtain quite high strengths from lightweight aggregate concrete. Paste strength (and hence water/cement ratio) is still an overriding influence; because of the larger water contents absorbed by the aggregates there can be major differences between total and free water/cement ratios and complications that arise through use of the former make it desirable, if at all possible, to use the latter, even though it may be rather approximate. The relation between strength and water/cement ratio is also a function of the type and volume concentration of aggregate. Since in practice the free water/cement ratio is never precisely known and since total water/cement ratio is not really relevant, it is probably better to relate strength to cement content at a particular level of workability. This is very useful for mix design purposes and, indeed, this is what Fig. 9.1 does. It is based on the use of typical materials with mixes of 'medium' workability; for higher or lower workabilities the strength could be expected to be somewhat lower and higher respectively. Adjustment of mix proportions could also lead to reduction in water requirements for workability and hence an increase in strength for a given cement content.

The data for Leca apply to Leca coarse aggregate and natural sand; if Leca fines are used the strength would be less, for a given cement content, by about 7 N/mm^2. Because of the lightness and porosity of this aggregate (which make it extremely useful in the lower strength range) there is a fairly low ceiling strength for this concrete, of the order of about 30 to 35 N/mm^2. Ceiling strengths for the others are much higher and are probably about 60 to 70 N/mm^2.

Foamed slag probably benefits most from the inclusion of natural sand and much better strength/cement content relations can be found than if all foamed slag aggregate mixes are used.

As cement content increases so does the density of the concrete and quite a useful relation can then be established between strength and density for each type of aggregate.

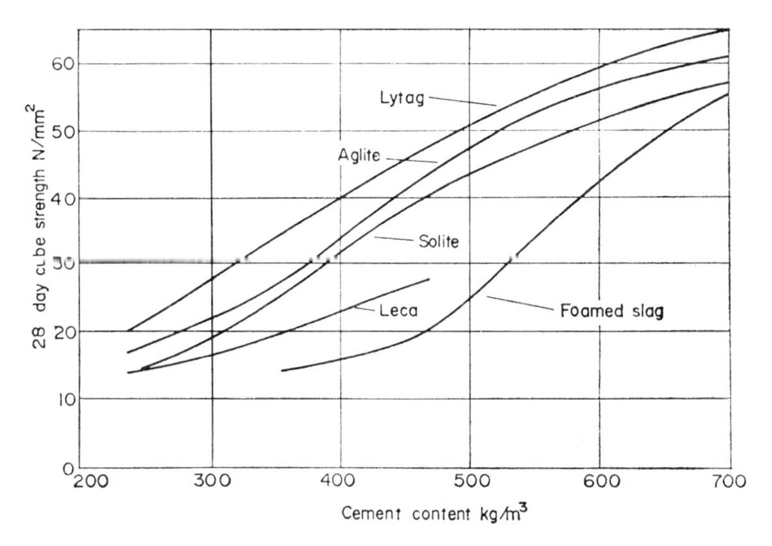

FIG. 9.1 Typical relation between cube strength and cement content for different lightweight aggregate concretes.

9.6.2 Tensile strength

Observations similar to those regarding normal concrete apply here; in principle similar factors play a similar role in determining the different aspects of tensile strength and the relations between compressive and tensile strengths are closely in accord with the points made in Section 3.3. Lightweight aggregate concrete tends to resemble crushed rock concrete rather more than gravel concrete but the range of values for all the types of concrete is so wide as to make this of little practical importance.

It may be noted that ceiling strengths are naturally lower and, for some aggregates, in certain tests fracture of the aggregate particles may affect the result obtained quite significantly.

While curing conditions, other than in water, may affect different concretes in different ways, for water-stored specimens of given compressive strength similar flexural and indirect tensile strength may be taken for normal and lightweight aggregate concrete.[29]

9.6.3 Deformation

Overall deformation of unreinforced lightweight aggregate concrete is likely to be considerably greater than that of normal concrete of similar strength subjected to similar loading and environment. The modulus of elasticity can be taken as 0·5 to 0·7 times that of normal concrete of similar strength.

Creep and drying shrinkage, while probably occurring at different rates and being more reflective of relative humidity, are likely to be perhaps twice the magnitude of that of comparable normal concrete, although the range for the latter will overlap that for the lightweight material.

Despite the foregoing observations, which apply to plain concrete, the presence of reinforcement, the structural configuration and relatively massive sizes of many elements may considerably alter the behaviour so that the final deformation may not be much greater than that of the normal concrete. The design engineer should certainly not find the problems too daunting and deformation should not cause undue worry. It is, of course, doubly important to follow the good practice of establishing the characteristics specific to each material to be used and not to rely too indiscriminately on generalised data.

9.6.4 Durability

Aggregate porosity should not be taken as being synonymous with porous concrete and experience has shown that properly proportioned, fully compacted lightweight aggregate concrete exhibits adequate durability and compares quite reasonably with very good quality normal concrete.[29] It is desirable to have sufficient cover to reinforcement to prevent likely moisture movement from the external surface, through a coarse aggregate particle, to the steel, causing serious corrosion problems; thus rather more cover is required, especially for corrosive conditions.

9.7 MIX DESIGN

The same principles apply here as for normal concrete, but the selection of mix proportions is rather more arbitrary.

Basically the approach recommended, for initial trial mixes, is:

(1) For a given type of aggregate, select the approximate cement content, compatible with strength and durability criteria, from Fig. 9.1.

(2) Use Fig. 9.2 to convert cement content to aggregate/cement ratio by volume.

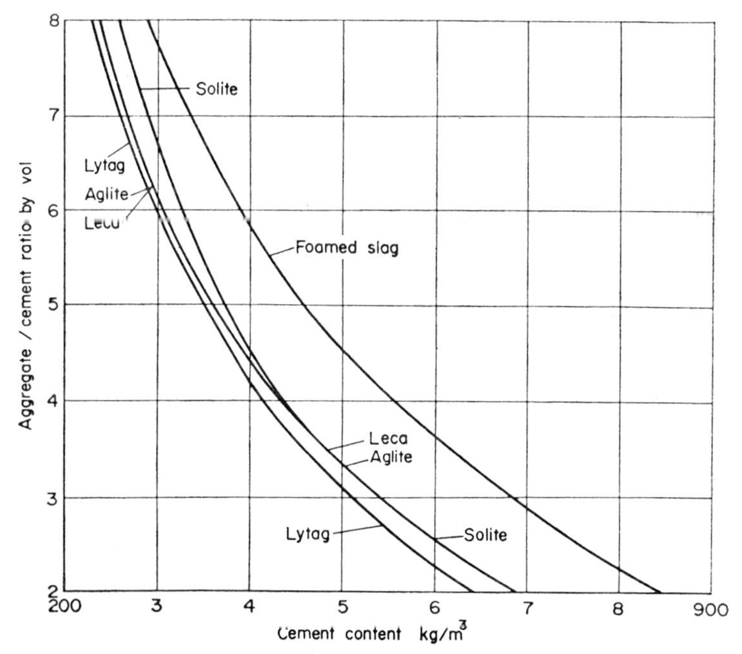

FIG. 9.2 Typical relation between aggregate/cement ratio (by volume) and cement content for different lightweight aggregate concretes.

(3) Knowing the bulk density of the aggregates, convert aggregate/cement ratio by volume to weight.

(4) From data provided, unless more accurate information is available, obtain the required water content (kg/m^3) for workability.

(5) Choose the fine/coarse aggregate ratio; this will usually be 50/50 by volume, but can be profitably adjusted for richness,

aggregate characteristics, and so on. (In fact, it can range from about 25/75 to 65/35, but for preliminary purposes it is suggested that it be taken as 40/60 for Lytag and 50/50 for others, for normal cement contents.)

(6) Having computed the weights of each ingredient required, water is added until the desired workability is judged to have been obtained. The mix is then checked, in the usual way, and necessary modifications are applied using the results.

Table 9.1 gives some data suitable for preliminary purposes.

TABLE 9.1

Data for preliminary mixes using lightweight aggregates

Aggregate	Dry, loose bulk density (kg/m^3)		Water content for trial mix[a] (kg/m^3)	Wet density of concrete (kg/m^3)
	Fine	Coarse		
Aglite	1 000–1 070	650–720	300	1 630–1 790
Foamed slag	850–950	650–750	325	1 820–2 100
Lytag	1 000–1 200	750–870	315	1 700–1 840
Leca	700–750	380–480	250	1 230–1 470[b]
Solite	880–1 000	560–720	250	1 650–1 800

[a] Total water, based on dry aggregates; if wet aggregates are used then this would have to be increased appropriately. The workability corresponds to 'medium' level.

[b] Leca coarse and fine aggregates; with natural sand this would be about 1 500 to 1 760 kg/m^3.

Despite the observations in Section 9.6.1 about total water/cement ratio, total water contents are given in Table 9.1 because they are meant only as a very approximate guide, are more easily computed and are not related to strength—water/cement relations.

9.7.1 Example

A mix is required to have a characteristic strength of 25 N/mm^2 at 28 days and medium workability. Lytag aggregate is to be used, the dry, loose bulk density being 1 040 and 800 kg/m^3 of fines and coarse respectively.

(1) For the control envisaged let us say that the design mean strength should be $(25 + 9)\ N/mm^2$, *i.e.* 34 N/mm^2.

(2) From Fig. 9.1 this leads to a cement content of 355 kg/m^3.

(3) From Fig. 9.2 an aggregate/cement ratio, by volume, of about 5:1 is obtained.

(4) Because this aggregate usually has good particle shape and rather a lot of fly ash in the fines, we may choose 40/60 by volume for the fines/coarse ratio.

(5) Converting from volume proportions of 1:2:3 (cement:fines: coarse aggregate) we obtain weight proportions of 1:1·44:1·66.

(6) Water is added to obtain the desired workability and this may be somewhat different from the 315 kg/m^3 shown in Table 9.1.

9.7.2 Specific gravity factor

For purposes of modifying mixes it is useful to calculate the absolute volume proportions of the ingredients so that selected ones may be changed or held constant as desired. But with lightweight aggregates, as previously discussed, there are difficulties in measuring specific gravities with sufficient accuracy and hence 'specific gravity factors' have been suggested as an alternative.[30]

A specific gravity factor is calculated for an aggregate used in a particular moisture condition and applies only to that aggregate in that condition; it is specific to the actual condition of the material as used and changes as the condition and/or the material changes. Within that limitation it can be used quite successfully in a way similar to that in which specific gravity can be used for normal aggregates. The following example illustrates the method.

Table 9.2 shows data, from Section 9.7.1, for the trial mix.

TABLE 9.2

Data for trial Lytag mix from Section 9.7.1

Ingredient	Weights for trial mix batch of 1 m^3 (kg)	Actual weights used (kg)	Weight per m^3 (kg[a])	Absolute volume (litres/m^3)
Cement	355	355	348	110
Dry fines	510	510	500	—
Dry coarse	588	588	580	—
Water	315	328	320	320
Air	—	—	—	25

[a] Measured wet density = 1 740 kg/m^3; batch weight = 1 781 kg; therefore volume of batch = 1 781/1 740 = 1·02 m^3.

The water content was increased from 315 to 328 kg/m^3 and the actual measured wet bulk density was 1 740 kg/m^3 (as compared to the expected value of 1 781 kg/m^3, being the sum of the actual weights of ingredients used). The weights of material per cubic metre of concrete are:

$$\text{cement } 355 \times \frac{1\,740}{1\,781} = 348 \text{ kg}$$

$$\text{fines} \quad 348 \times 1{\cdot}44 = 500 \text{ kg}$$

$$\text{coarse} \quad 348 \times 1{\cdot}66 = 580 \text{ kg}$$

$$\text{water} \quad 328 \times \frac{1\,740}{1\,781} = 320 \text{ kg}$$

The absolute volumes of the ingredients are:

cement 348/3·15 = 110 l/m^3

water = 320 l/m^3

air 2·5%* $= \frac{25}{455}$ l/m^3 of concrete

the absolute volume of the aggregate = 1 000 − 455 = 545 l

Assuming that the fines/coarse ratio by absolute volume is equal to that by bulk volume (it may not be, of course, but is reasonably close to it), then:

fines 0·40 × 545 = 218 l

coarse 0·60 × 545 = 327 l

therefore specific gravity factor = 500/218 for the fines
= 2·29

and = 580/327 for the coarse
= 1·77

To re-proportion a mix, using similar materials (and specifically using aggregates as they were in the trial mix) and possessing similar

* This is reasonable for lightweight aggregate concrete.

workability, but requiring a cement content of, say, 295 kg/m^3, these factors can be utilised thus:

cement content 295 kg/m^3 — 94 l/m^3 (absolute volume)
water content 320 kg/m^3 — 320 l/m^3 (absolute volume)

(maintained constant for the same workability)

air 2·5% — $\frac{25}{439}$ l absolute volume per m^3 of concrete

aggregate volume = 1 000 − 439 = 561 l/m^3
fines: 0·40 × 561 = 224 l ≡ 224 × 2·29 kg
= 510 kg
coarse: 0·60 × 561 = 337 l ≡ 337 × 1·77 kg
= 600 kg

The new mix is then

295:510:600:320 (cement:fines:coarse:water)

or

1:1·71:2·02:1·08 by weight

Had the Lytag been used, for example, in a saturated condition, the total water content chosen for the preliminary trial would have been different from that based on dry aggregates (namely 315 kg/m^3)—and might have been of the order of 360 kg/m^3—and therefore the wet density of the concrete would be higher because of the greater amount of water inside the saturated aggregate pores as compared to that inside the initially dry aggregate pores; this obviously would affect the cement content (kg/m^3) and hence the alleged absolute volume of aggregate per cubic metre of concrete with a consequently different value of specific gravity factor for fine and coarse fractions.

Clearly, there is no difficulty in arriving at appropriate values of the factors for any condition of the aggregate; they should not be misused by incorrect application.

Chapter 10

MIX DESIGN FOR TENSILE STRENGTH

10.1 INTRODUCTION

In Chapter 3, Sections 3.3 and 3.4, some aspects of tensile strength were briefly discussed and some points were noted about the two main test methods used. Perhaps it is worth emphasising that when concrete 'fails'—and the exact nature of the failure phenomenon and the philosophy underlying this need not concern us here—*i.e.* when, in an engineering sense, it has cracked, this is almost invariably because its tensile strength has been exceeded; tensile stresses (or accompanying tensile deformation) have been too high. The compressive strength of concrete is very much higher (say ten to twenty times) than its tensile strength and therefore under most conditions in service it is likely that the latter will be the parameter of prime importance.

In rigid pavement structures—concrete roads and airfield runways—while compressive strength is probably a reflection of the likely durability (apart from effects of frost and salt), it seems logical, from the stresses assumed to be induced from, for example, traffic and temperature effects, to treat tensiie strength as the more relevant structural parameter. This does not seem to be entirely borne out by observations of full-scale roads and there is a certain ambiguity evident in various assessments; however, current trends do seem to favour the use of tensile strengths and there is a need, therefore, for data allowing mixes to be selected on this basis.

10.2 FLEXURAL STRENGTH

Excellent data are available in the work done by Wright[31] and it is possible to select mixes, quite rationally, using these as a guide. Some points worth noting are:

(a) beams may be tested more conveniently on their sides rather than in the direction of casting; the former is now permitted by BS 1881:1970 and the results obtained are not significantly affected;

(b) the result obtained is a function of the rate of loading (as it is for all tests) and Wright established that there is a linear relation between the modulus of rupture, or flexural strength, and the logarithm of the rate of increase of stress; for instance, a change in the rate of stressing from 0·3 to 1·5 N/mm^2 results in about 9% increase in ultimate flexural strength;

(c) the type of aggregate can have a predominant effect, crushed rock aggregates resulting in concretes with higher flexural strengths than gravel aggregates, for comparable mixes, assuming that sound materials are used. Although aggregates of one type but from different sources will tend to exhibit somewhat different strengths, it can generally be assumed that the differences between these will probably be less than the differences between different types of aggregate. Thus, it is convenient to group gravels together, separately from crushed rocks, and the data is representative of typical values likely to be encountered in practice.

10.2.1 Increase of flexural strength with age

Most mix design data, with usual specifications in mind, emphasise 28-day strength requirements but, of course, it is frequently useful, or essential, to have data for other ages, certainly for quality control purposes. Table 10.1 gives data, based on Road Research Technical

TABLE 10.1

Gain in flexural strength with age of typical concretes

Aggregate type	28-day strength (N/mm^2)	Percent of 28-day strength at 7 days	28 days	3 months	1 year
Gravel and sand	4·5	89	100	114	128
	4·0	89	100	114	130
	3·5	86	100	116	134
	3·0	81	100	117	131
Crushed rock and sand	6·0	83	100	112	117
	5·0	81	100	118	124
	4·5	77	100	117	127
	4·0	74	100	120	132

Paper No. 67,[31] for concretes of four different strength levels, in terms of their 28-day strengths and for two types of aggregates, namely gravels (rounded and irregular being grouped together) and crushed rocks.

10.2.2 Relation between flexural and compressive strengths

The general form of this relation has been mentioned in Section 3.3 and an analysis of Wright's data allows Fig. 10.1 to be drawn which shows, for 28-day cube and beam strengths, typical comparisons for

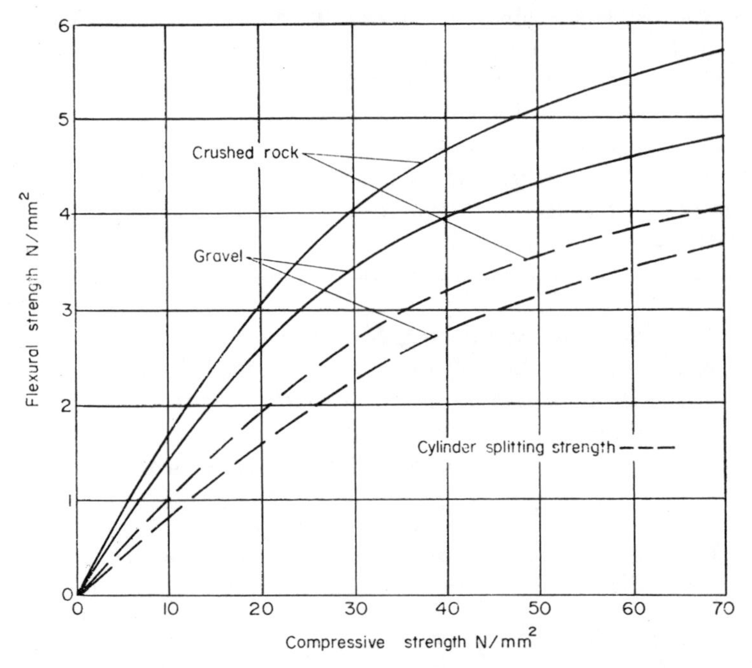

FIG. 10.1 Typical relation between flexural and compressive strengths for gravel and crushed rock aggregate concretes (based on Ref. 31).

gravel and crushed rock concretes. There is evidence to suggest that this relation is largely independent of age, certainly until ages at which the ceiling strengths of the concretes are being approached. The significant difference between the two types of concrete is readily apparent and the tendency towards limiting flexural strengths is also clearly shown.

10.2.3 Relation between flexural strength and water/cement ratio

Although Wright found that the strength obtained at a given water/cement ratio was dependent upon the level of workability of the concrete, a study of his data indicates that, for practical purposes, it is permissible to ignore this and so Fig. 10.2 shows the relation between 28-day flexural strength and nominal free water/cement ratio for rounded and irregular gravel and crushed rock coarse

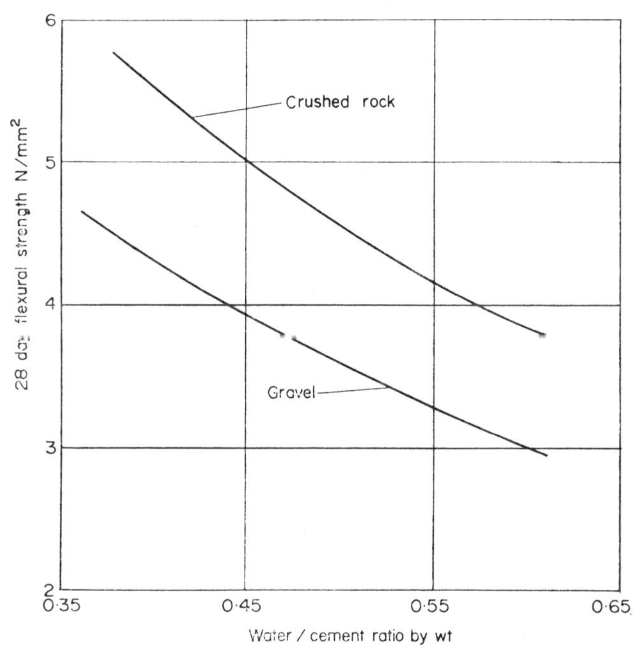

FIG. 10.2 Typical relation between 28-day flexural strength and water/cement ratio for gravel and crushed rock aggregate concrete (based on Ref. 31).

aggregates, each combined with a natural pit sand. The figure shows the approximate order of strength likely to be obtained and the influence of the type of coarse aggregate. The effect of the latter may be different at later ages and, indeed, the inclusion of fine aggregates other than natural pit sands (for example, the use of crushed limestone fines) may also affect the relation.

10.2.4 Relation between aggregate/cement ratio and flexural strength

Figure 10.3 shows a rather more useful relation than that shown in Fig. 10.2; it shows aggregate/cement ratio by weight plotted against

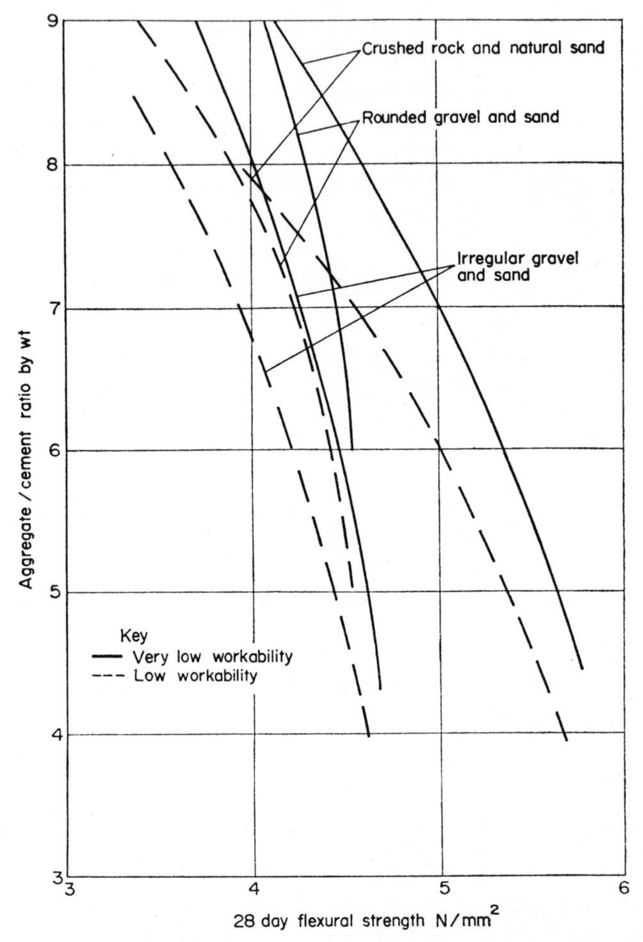

FIG. 10.3 Typical relation between aggregate/cement ratio (by weight) and 28-day flexural strengths for very low and low workability.

28-day flexural strength for very low and low workability (compacting factors 0·78 and 0·85 respectively). These levels of workability were chosen specifically with concrete pavement structures in mind and not the usual concrete structures; the former would usually be compacted by means whereby such workability would be most suitable. It will be noted that, for a given flexural strength, as the workability decreases so the aggregate/cement ratio increases. Thus for a strength of 4·0 N/mm^2:

Type of aggregate	Workability very low	low
	(Aggregate/cement ratio by weight)	
Rounded	9·2	7·7
Irregular	8·0	6·7
Angular	9·4	7·9

There will usually be a limiting cement content (and thus aggregate/cement ratio, for a particular type of aggregate) permitted by the concrete specification; if this, for example, were to be 7·0:1, the effect on the strengths obtained can be seen:

Type of Aggregate	Workability very low	low
	[28-day flexural strength (N/mm^2)]	
Rounded	4·4	4·2
Irregular	4·3	3·9
Angular	5·0	4·5

10.2.5 Mix design

The process of mix design is essentially the same, in principle, as that discussed in Chapter 4, but the type of aggregate has an important role and should not be overlooked.

The relation between specified characteristic and design mean strengths is not so well established for flexural as for cube strengths and it is naturally best to build up experience and data to allow reliable estimates to be made. Wright[31] suggests using the Road Note No. 4 control factors, although he points out that these are almost certainly pessimistic. It has also been suggested[24] that a fixed margin be used, the magnitude of which depends upon the degree of quality control exercised on site, as for cubes, the minimum value being 0·55 N/mm^2 and, in the absence of supporting data, a value of 1·1 N/mm^2 being required.

10.2.6 Example

A mix is required to have 20·0 mm maximum size aggregate, low workability and a characteristic flexural strength of 3·0 N/mm^2 at

28 days. Either gravel (of irregular shape) or crushed rock (of angular shape) can be used, combined with natural sand. Good control is anticipated.

(1) The design mean strength can be taken as (3·0 + 0·8) N/mm^2 in this instance.

(2) If required, an estimate of the nominal free water/cement ratio can be obtained from Fig. 10.2; for gravel it is 0·47, for the crushed rock it is 0·60.

(3) The aggregate/cement ratio can be obtained from Fig. 10.3; for gravel it is 7·3, for the crushed rock it is 8·1.

Note that the higher the characteristic strength the greater the difference between the aggregate/cement ratios; for example, had the strength been 3·5 N/mm^2 and the design mean strength 4·3 N/mm^2, for the crushed rock mix the aggregate/cement ratio would have been 7·5 and for the gravel 5·8.

Had the concretes been specified in terms of a characteristic compressive strength of, say, 27·5 N/mm^2, with a design mean strength of, say, 37·5 N/mm^2, Figs. 4.1 and 4.3(a) would indicate that the appropriate aggregate/cement ratios were 6·4 for the gravel and about 6·1 for the crushed rock.

It is clear that designing on the basis of flexural rather than cube strengths may result in some difference in aggregate/cement ratio with a significant effect due to the type of aggregate used.

10.3 CYLINDER SPLITTING STRENGTH

Although this is not a uniaxial tensile strength test (a cylinder, already split and therefore having no tensile strength, replaced carefully in the testing machine will still carry some load and thus possess an apparent strength which is entirely due to the test conditions), it seems to be closely related to that parameter(22) and is thus very useful. It seems likely(32) that it will be specified as a control test for major concrete roads.

There are indications(33,34) that a number of factors can significantly affect the apparent ultimate strength; amongst these are:

the type and width of packing strips;
the absence of packing strips;
the size of the specimen;
the correct alignment of the specimen in the test machine;

the type of lubricant, if any, used in the ball-seating of the test machine.

Section 3.4 gives the method used for computing the alleged tensile stress at failure of the splitting test.

10.3.1 Effect of water/cement ratio

Figure 10.4, based on data given by Franklin and King,[32] shows the relation between cylinder splitting strength and nominal free water/cement ratio for crushed rock and gravel aggregate concretes and again it is seen that the effect of the aggregate can be quite significant.

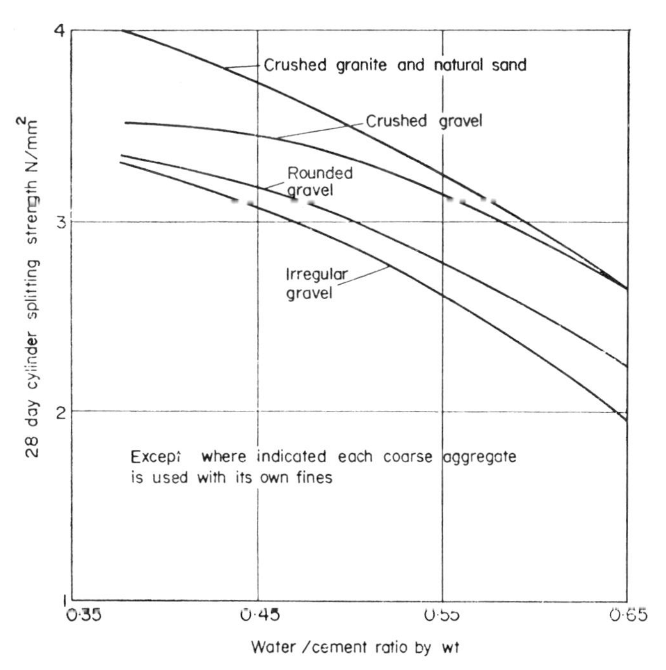

FIG. 10.4 Typical relations between cylinder splitting strength and water/cement ratio for gravel and crushed rock aggregate concretes (based on Ref. 32).

10.3.2 Effect of age

The cylinder splitting/age relation is very like that observed for the flexural strength, except that the magnitude of the former is less than that of the latter. Table 10.2 gives data, based on R.R.L. Report LR 412.[32]

TABLE 10.2

Gain in cylinder splitting strength with age of typical concretes

Aggregate types	28-day strength (N/mm^2)	Percent of 28-day strength at 7 days	28 days	3 months	1 year
Rounded gravel	2·5	80	100	119	127
Irregular or angular gravel	3·0	79	100	115	123
Crushed rock	3·5	80	100	117	125

10.3.3 Relation between cylinder splitting and compressive strength

The curves showing the above relation are of a type similar to those for the flexural/compressive strength data (*see* Fig. 10.1). Again the effect of the aggregate is clearly shown and there is a significant increase in tensile strength, for a given compressive strength, with the angular, crushed aggregates.

10.3.4 Relation between aggregate/cement ratio and cylinder splitting strength

Using data from Franklin and King,[32] it is possible to plot aggregate/cement ratios by weight against cylinder splitting strength for concretes of 'V–B' times 8 ± 2 sec, *i.e.* of about low workability with compacting factors in the region of 0·85. Figure 10.5 shows the result. The aggregates were basically of rounded, irregular and angular particle shape (both coarse and fine fractions) except for the one indicated, which was a crushed rock, coarse aggregate combined with a rounded, natural sand.

It is interesting to note the effect of aggregate type on tensile strength (say, 3·0 N/mm^2):

Aggregate type	Rounded coarse and fines	Irregular coarse and fines	Angular coarse and fines	Angular coarse and rounded fines
a/c ratio	6·6	5·4	4·7	7·4

Clearly, the combination of crushed rock, coarse aggregate and a natural pit sand is beneficial and, depending upon materials' cost, haulage and so on, it would seem to be the best solution. It should

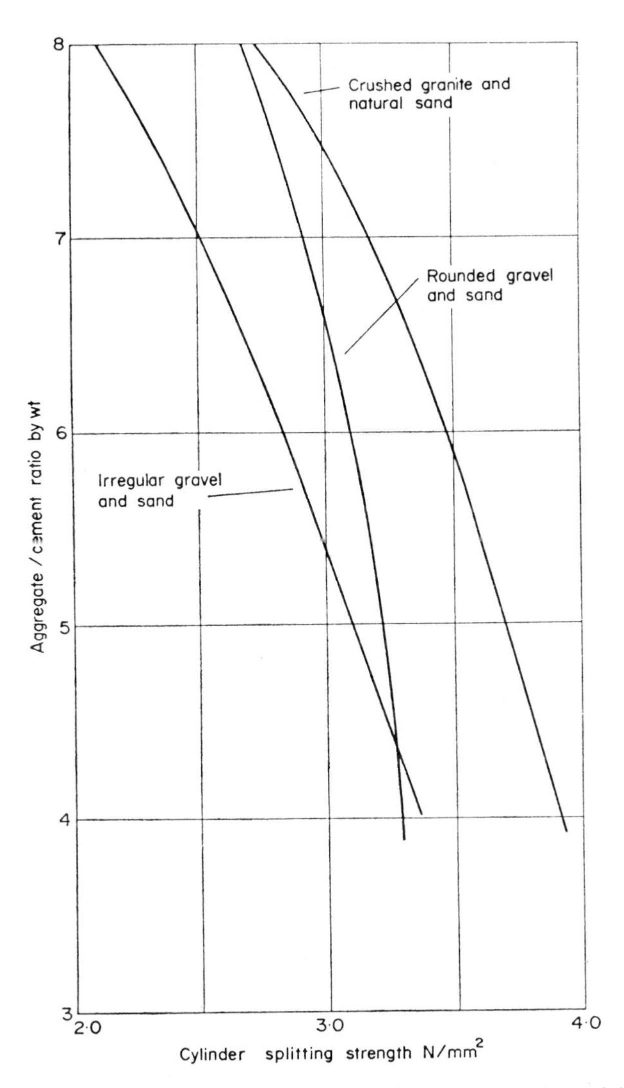

FIG. 10.5 Typical relation between aggregate/cement ratio (by weight) and cylinder splitting strengths for different aggregate types in concrete of low workability (based on Ref. 32).

be noted that the other three aggregates are all gravels and this is probably related to the fact that there are fairly similar aggregate/cement ratios for the irregular and angular ones.

10.4 MIX DESIGN

It seems that for roads the specified characteristic tensile splitting strength may be about 1·8 N/mm^2.[32] Margins between this and the design mean strength may be 0·35 N/mm^2 where there is evidence to support it or 0·70 N/mm^2 where there is no evidence of the level of quality control to be exercised, as suggested for structural concrete.[24]

The selection of mix proportions will be in accordance with well-established principles and Fig. 10.5 gives some guidance on choice of aggregate/cement ratio. Should lower workability be used, the data will be pessimistic; the aggregate/cement ratios will be a little lower than they could be. However, it is likely that durability considerations will prohibit taking advantage of excessively lean mixes and, instead, the higher tensile strength may be accepted as a useful bonus.

Chapter 11

THE USE OF STATISTICS IN MIX DESIGN

11.1 REALITY OBSERVED

When dealing with 'judgement' situations—for example, the likely reactions of a group of people to a particular style of newspaper; or the response of an audience to a musical composition; or the likely influence of choice of interior decoration on hotel occupants—most people accept a range of viewpoints. But when handling numbers or manipulating numerate data there is generally felt to be one answer, the 'true', exact answer. It is, of course, a truism that the mere operations carried out on the numbers must result in only one correct answer (the product of 3 and 7 must always be 21 once the numbers have been defined) but, fortunately, life is much more subtle than that and the really important aspect is the manner in which the numbers are obtained and the precision with which they are endowed. If there is any trace of doubt at all about the numerical values being operated upon, then naturally there must be some doubt about the final resulting number, even though the number is correct in terms of the arithmetic being performed.

Let us suppose that ready-mixed concrete is to be supplied to a particular site for some strip foundations. The dimensions given on the drawings quite clearly and precisely show the foundation as 0·6 m wide, 1·0 m deep and 20·0 m long, *i.e.* 12 m^3. However, the actual dimensions measured on site are found to be slightly different, so that when 12·0 m^3 of concrete, accurately batched, are delivered on site it is found that rather more is required. Thus the 12·0 m^3 is correct in terms of the product of the assumed dimensions, but the latter are not themselves correct and so the actual volume required is greater than 12·0 m^3. The magical exactitude of the numbers is not matched by the reality.

This lack of correspondence underlies the use of statistics and is a phenomenon that must be appreciated by anyone who wishes to properly interpret data based on measurement, because the act of measuring inevitably introduces a source of error, a degree of uncertainty, into the observed parameter.

11.2 THE MEAN VALUE

If a batch of concrete is made into a set of ten cubes and these are weighed and the summed weights divided by ten, this gives the mean weight of the set. It will be found that the ten individual weights are likely to show some variation in the values obtained; this will be partly because there is some real variation (owing to small changes in concrete composition from cube to cube and/or to small differences in volume, caused by inaccuracies in the moulds) and some apparent variation introduced by the method of weighing and the skill of the operator. If only three cubes were weighed then the average value of these would be an estimate (and only an estimate) of the set. Obviously, the more cubes weighed the more the average would approach the true mean of the entire set. There will always, therefore, be some doubt about the value found from a sample, but the doubt diminishes as the sample size increases.

The average is defined as

$$\bar{x} = (\Sigma\, x)/n$$

where $\bar{x}$ is the average value, $\Sigma\, x$ is the sum of the individual values and n is the number of values.

11.3 MEASURING VARIABILITY

Two sets of tensile strength results from different concretes are given below, using an experimental testing technique:

(1) N/mm^2	(2) N/mm^2	(1) N/mm^2	(2) N/mm^2
2·0	2·0	2·2	2·8
2·4	2·2	2·9	2·2
2·0	2·4	2·3	2·4
2·0	1·8	2·2	2·2
2·3	1·6	2·4	3·0
5·0	3·0	1·4	2·9

The average of (1) is 2·42 and of (2) is 2·37 N/mm^2; they are thus quite close in terms of average strength. However, this does not give us all the required information on each set.

The *range* (*i.e.* the difference between maximum and minimum values) can readily be found for each and is (5·0 − 1·4) = 3·6 N/mm^2 for (1) and (3·0 − 1·6) = 1·4 N/mm^2 for (2). There is some difference here but this is unduly influenced by the extreme values and takes no account of all the others. It is thus unreliable and inefficient. The *standard deviation*, on the other hand, takes each value into account and is a measure of the deviation of each result from the average value. It is not biased particularly towards any individual value but is influenced by them all. It is defined as

$$\sigma = \left[\frac{\Sigma\,(x - \bar{x})^2}{n}\right]^{\frac{1}{2}}$$

where σ is the standard deviation (N/mm^2), x is the individual value (N/mm^2), $\bar{x}$ is the average value and n is the number of results.

In practice the true standard deviation is not likely to be known since not all the concrete will be tested and so the measured value is usually distinguished from the theoretical one by showing the former as 's'; there is also a refinement applied which is a correction allowing for the fact that s, calculated from a smaller sample, will be less than the true value σ; thus

$$s = \left[\frac{\Sigma\,(x - \bar{x})^2}{n - 1}\right]^{\frac{1}{2}}$$

where the symbols are as before.

The value of s approaches σ for large values of n and the denominator can then be changed from $(n - 1)$ to n. For practical purposes it seems debatable to introduce this refinement into data such as those resulting from tests on concrete or similar variable materials, because the inherent variation is quite high and the inference underlying such a correction presupposes a degree of accuracy and reliability not generally in keeping with such test results. However, it is general practice to adopt this procedure and codes of practice[2,24] and specifications[35] certainly advocate it; therefore, it is probably better, for consistency, to follow suit.

Another way of expressing the standard deviation is

$$s = \left[\frac{\Sigma x^2 - [(\Sigma x)^2/n]}{n-1}\right]^{\frac{1}{2}}$$

which has the advantage that $\bar{x}$ does not have to be calculated; this is important in calculating standard deviations on accumulating data, and is also more convenient on the normal, older-fashioned calculating machines, but not necessarily on electronic machines.

The standard deviations of sets (1) and (2), p. 128, are worked out to illustrate the process:

Set (1)		Set (2)	
x (N/mm^2)	x^2	x (N/mm^2)	x^2
2·0	4·00	2·0	4·00
2·4	5·76	2·2	4·84
2·0	4·00	2·4	5·76
2·0	4·00	1·8	3·24
2·3	5·29	1·6	2·56
5·0	25·00	3·0	9·00
2·2	4·84	2·8	7·84
2·9	8·41	2·2	4·84
2·3	5·29	2·4	5·76
2·2	4·84	2·2	4·84
2·4	5·76	3·0	9·00
1·4	1·96	2·9	8·41
29·1 Σx	79·15 Σx^2	28·5 Σx	70·09 Σx^2

$$s_1 = \left(\frac{79{\cdot}15 - [(29{\cdot}1)^2/12]}{11}\right)^{\frac{1}{2}} = 0{\cdot}91 \text{ N/mm}^2 \qquad s_2 = \left(\frac{70{\cdot}09 - [(28{\cdot}5)^2/12]}{11}\right)^{\frac{1}{2}} = 0{\cdot}47 \text{ N/mm}^2$$

Since s_1 is roughly twice s_2 it is apparent that the variation within the former is the higher. Because the average strengths of these two sets are similar it is reasonable and useful to compare the variation on the basis of the standard deviation of each. However, should it be necessary to compare two sets, produced under 'identical' conditions, of different levels of average strength, it might not be so useful to use this parameter. For example, if set (1) and another set,

set (3) with an average strength of 4·05 N/mm², were to be compared and if the standard deviation of the latter was 1·42 N/mm², then this would hardly reflect the level of supervision and control exercised over the production of the test specimens. However, if the *coefficient of variation* is checked this may be a more reliable reflection. This is defined as

$$V = \frac{s}{\bar{x}} \times 100$$

where V is the coefficient of variation (%), s is the standard deviation (N/mm²) and $\bar{x}$ is the average strength (N/mm²).

Thus, for set (1)

$$V_1 = \frac{0{\cdot}91}{2{\cdot}42} \times 100 = 37{\cdot}5\%$$

and for set (3)

$$V_3 = \frac{1{\cdot}42}{4{\cdot}05} \times 100 = 35{\cdot}0\%$$

and this seems to be a better indication of the variation. The coefficient of variation is therefore useful when, for a given degree of control, the variation of sets of significantly different average strengths is to be assessed.

It may be observed here that recommended values of standard deviation for indirect tensile strengths, for mix design purposes, are about 0·18 to 0·35 N/mm², depending upon the availability of supporting data.[24] Therefore, the variability of strengths in sets (1) and (2) is too high and the testing technique is unacceptable, assuming that the fabrication of the specimens was in order.

11.4 THE GAUSSIAN OR NORMAL DISTRIBUTION

If cube strength results are grouped in intervals of, say, 2·0 N/mm² and the number of cubes with strengths in each interval is counted, this can be shown graphically by plotting the latter against strength and a histogram is obtained. Figure 11.1 shows a typical histogram for the following data:

Strength (N/mm^2)	No. of cubes in interval
20–22	1
22–24	3
24–26	0
26–28	9
28–30	29
30–32	40
32–34	49
34–36	70
36–38	54
38–40	46
40–42	31
42–44	11
44–46	0
46–48	6
48–50	1

The outline of the plot is approximately bell-shaped and it can be shown that as the number of cubes tested increases so the plot becomes more like a smooth curve; with really large numbers the curve becomes the normal or Gaussian curve as in Fig. 11.2. This is useful because it allows rather simple manipulation of data and prediction of likely behaviour without recourse to complex mathematics. It is completely defined by two parameters, the average and standard deviation.

The extremities of this curve extend to infinity and therefore, theoretically, it is certain that any cube result will be inside the boundary of the curve. In other words, the probability that any result will be between the minimum and maximum values at the extremities is one. (If there was a one in two chance we would say the probability was one half.) Thus, if the area under the curve is taken to be unity, the probability of a result being between two strength values (or within a particular strength interval) is equal to the area under the curve bounded by the ordinates at those two values expressed as a fraction of the total area under the curve. Figure 11.2 shows a typical distribution curve for a set of results, the average value of which is 35 N/mm^2. The hatched area between 30·5 and 35 N/mm^2 is 0·34 times the area under the whole curve and therefore the probability of a cube strength being within that interval

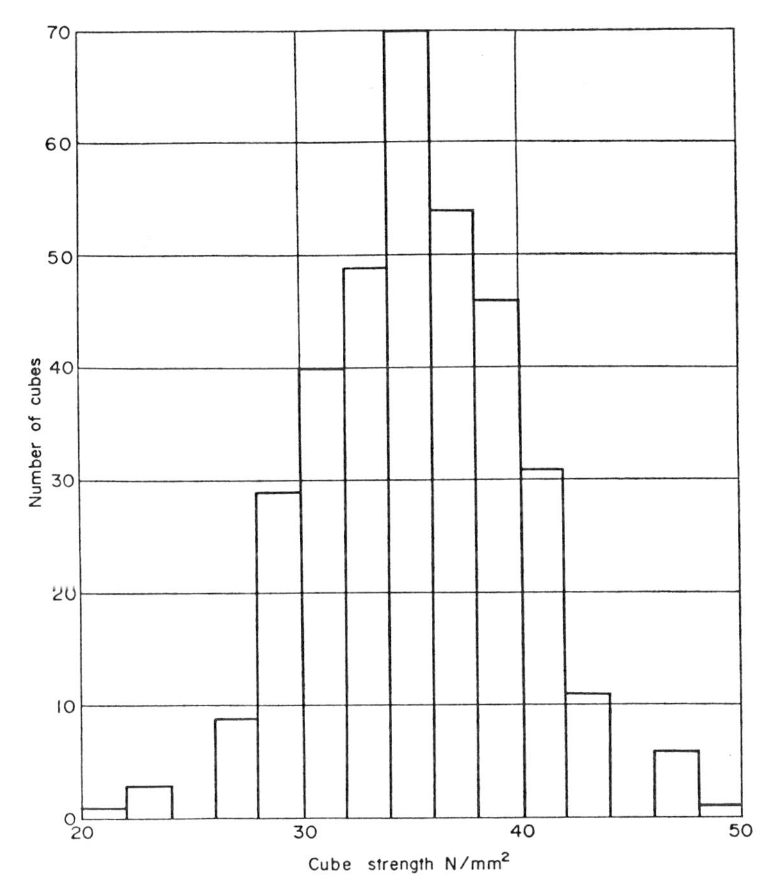

FIG. 11.1 Typical histogram of cube strengths.

is 34% or almost 1 in 3. On the other hand, the probability of a result being between the lower end of the curve (shown here as effectively 21·5 N/mm^2; in practice, of course, it could be lower than this, perhaps as low as say 10 N/mm^2, but hardly as low as minus infinity!) and 24·5 N/mm^2 is only about 1%, which is the relative area under the curve, bounded by 21·5, or a lower value, and 24·5 N/mm^2.

Therefore, knowing the properties of the particular normal distribution curve available, it is possible to compute the likelihood of cubes being within given strength levels or, more usefully and for most purposes, being less than a given strength value. Fortunately there are statistical tables available which allow the probability to be readily calculated (*see* Section 11.5).

Although the extremities of any Gaussian distribution curve do not meet the strength axis except, theoretically, at infinity, very little is lost if they are assumed to extend to $\pm 3s$ from the average $\bar{x}$, *i.e.*

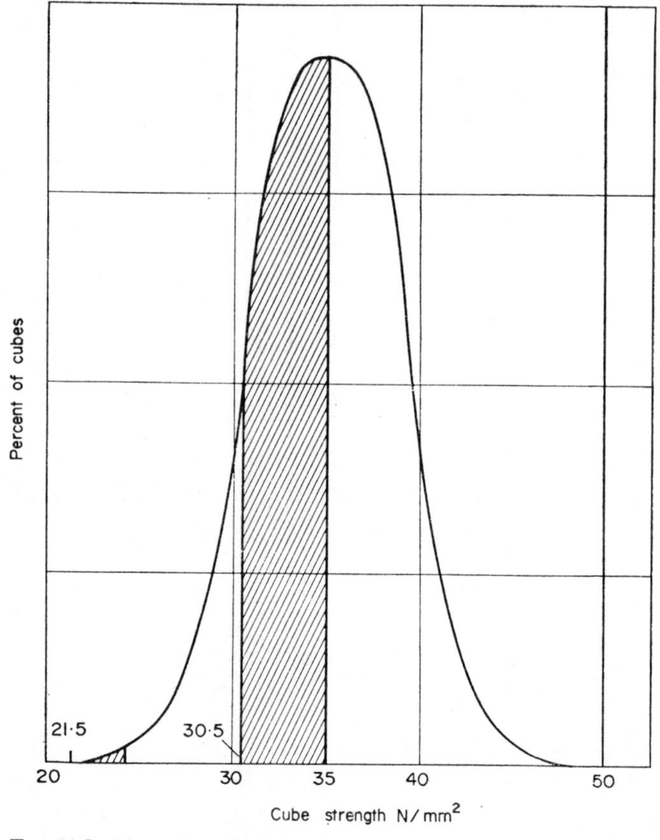

FIG. 11.2 Normal or Gaussian distribution curve of cube strengths.

the lower end $= \bar{x} - 3s$ and the upper end $= \bar{x} + 3s$, where s is the standard deviation of the set and $\bar{x}$ is the average strength of the set.

Effectively, the 'spread' of the curve is six times the standard deviation ($6s$). Because the geometry of the curve is fixed by the values of s and $\bar{x}$ (the areas under different curves applicable to

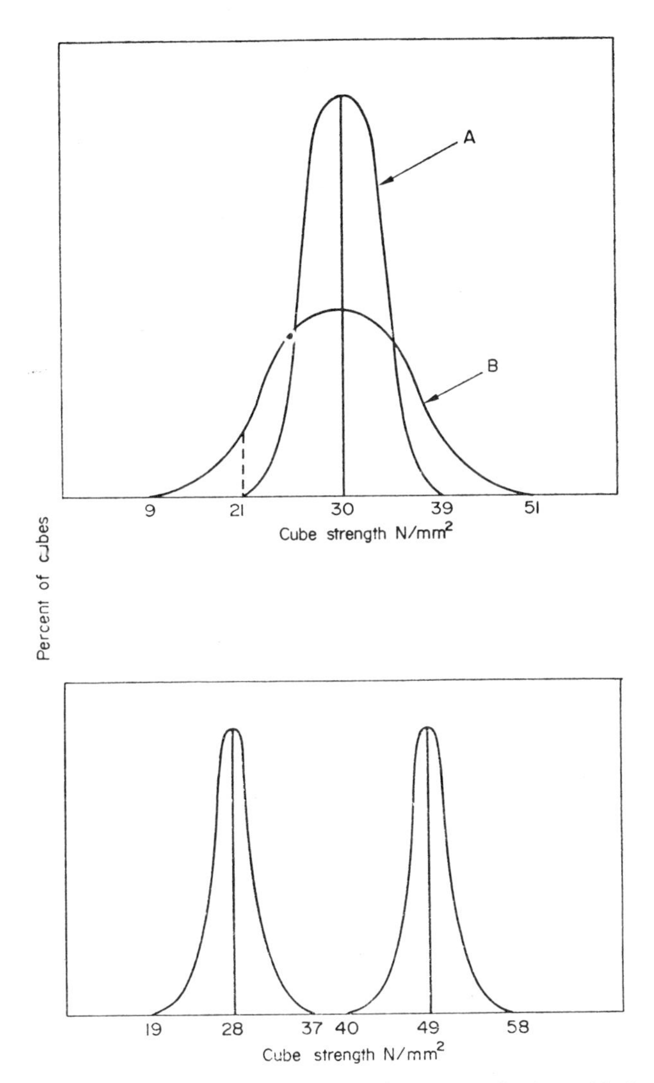

FIG. 11.3 (a) Normal distribution curves of two sets of cubes with the same average strength but different standard deviations. (b) Normal distribution curves of two sets of cubes with different average strengths but the same standard deviation.

concretes of similar average strength are equal) the 'squatness' changes as the values of s change. Thus, Fig. 11.3(a) shows two curves for concretes with the same average strength, 30 N/mm^2, but the standard deviation of set A is 3 N/mm^2 and of set B is 7 N/mm^2. Therefore, the spread of the former will be from about 21 to 39 N/mm^2 and of the latter 9 to 51 N/mm^2. The probability of a result being less than, say, 22 N/mm^2 will obviously be very small for set A but much more likely for set B (as is seen from the relative areas bounded by the curves, the ordinate at 22 N/mm^2 and the strength axis). Figure 11.3(b) represents the situation for two different concretes, average strengths 28 and 49 N/mm^2, each with a standard deviation of 3 N/mm^2.

11.5 CHARACTERISTIC AND AVERAGE STRENGTHS

The characteristic strength is that strength below which not more than a stated proportion of the test results should fall. This proportion is sometimes as low as 1%[35] or, more usually for structural concrete, 2½% or even 5%.[24] Once this acceptability has been defined, it is possible to choose a compatible mean strength for the mix design using the expression

$$x_0 = \bar{x} - ks$$

where x_0 is the characteristic strength (N/mm^2), $\bar{x}$ is the design mean strength, s is the standard deviation and k is a probability factor, associated with the definition of x_0, the value being obtained from statistical tables for Gaussian distribution curves (refer to Section 11.4).

Table 11.1 gives some values of k for different proportions of 'defective' cubes. The term 'defective' is used rather than 'failures' because the latter has strong connotations of unacceptability which are belied by the definition of characteristic strength. In the long run, if both the average strength and the standard deviation are of the anticipated values there will be the expected proportion of cubes less than the characteristic strength; this will merely be the confirmation that the statistics are correct and not a reflection on the dubious quality of the concrete.

It should be emphasised that the values of k could conveniently and realistically be rounded off to one decimal place since the number of test results available is usually rather small and the variability rather high in comparison with many other fields in science or technology where techniques are more sophisticated, where control is more refined and where large numbers of test results are analysed.

TABLE 11.1

Values of the probability factor k *for different proportions of cubes less than the characteristic strength*

Proportion of cubes less than the characteristic strength 1 in	per cent	k
6	16	1·00
10	10	1·28
20	5	1·64
25	4	1·75
33	3	1·88
40	2·5	1·96
50	2	2·05
100	1	2·33

The value of s is a function of the quality control exercised and may usually be between about 3·5 and 7·5 N/mm² for cubes,[24] but may be even greater for very poor control. Appropriate values are also given for flexural and tensile splitting test results.

Values of s for given quality control conditions are suggested below:

Degree of control	Standard deviation s (N/mm²)
Laboratory	2·0–3·5
Excellent site	3·5–4·5
Average site	5·0–6·0
Poor site	7·0–8·0+

It is naturally better to base the choice of s on data collected from previous relevant projects rather than to merely guess; should the latter be necessary, it is advisable that the value should not be too optimistic. The value of the design mean strength can then be settled. Referring to the symbols used in Section 4.2.2:

$$\bar{\mu} = \mu_0 + k_1$$

$\bar{\mu}$ being the same as $\bar{x}$ (the design mean strength), μ_0 being the same as x_0 (the specified characteristic strength) and k_1 being the same as ks.

For a given level of quality control the design mean strength will depend upon the definition of the specified characteristic strength and consequently so will mix proportions, for a given degree of workability. Some data are given below for a concrete containing irregular gravel aggregate of 20·0 mm size, with medium workability and a specified characteristic strength of 20 N/mm^2:

Standard deviation (N/mm^2)			
4·0		8·0	
Proportion of cubes less than characteristic strength (per cent)			
1·0	2·5	1·0	2·5
Design mean strength (N/mm^2)			
29·3	27·8	38·6	35·7
Approximate aggregate/cement ratio by weight			
6·3	6·5	5·3	5·7

Once the concrete production is under way, it is important to obtain, as quickly as possible, a reasonably reliable estimate of both $\bar{\mu}$ and s to check whether the previous assumptions are being confirmed. The minimum number of test results usually considered for this is forty; should the analysis show either s or $\bar{\mu}$ to be different from the values expected, immediate steps can be taken to change the situation. Taking the previous example, suppose that the expected average strength was 29·3 N/mm^2 with a standard deviation of 4·0 N/mm^2; if the on-site test results showed that the actual average was 29·0 N/mm^2 but the standard deviation was 6·0 N/mm^2, this would mean that unless the control was changed 1% of the results could be expected to be less than 29·0 – (2·33 × 6·0), *i.e.* 15·0 N/mm^2, and obviously more than that would be less than 20·0 N/mm^2, the specified characteristic strength. Likewise, if the standard deviation was 4·0 N/mm^2 but the average strength was only 25 N/mm^2, the expected 1% defective level would be 25·0 − (2·33 × 4·0), *i.e.* 15·7 N/mm^2. In the former case the mix would need to be redesigned for an average strength of 20·0 + (2·33 × 6·0) or 34·0 N/mm^2 and in the latter case the standard deviation would have to be reduced to (25·0 − 20·0)/2·33 *i.e.* 2·1 N/mm^2. It is highly unlikely that this standard deviation could be achieved and, much more realistically, the cause of the reduced average strength should be deduced and eliminated.

REFERENCES

1. THE COUNCIL FOR CODES OF PRACTICE. The structural use of reinforced concrete in buildings, CP 114 (1957, reset and reprinted 1965). London, British Standards Institution, pp. 95.
2. THE COUNCIL FOR CODES OF PRACTICE. The structural use of precast concrete, CP 116 (1965). London, British Standards Institution, pp. 153.
3. GLANVILLE, W. H., COLLINS, A. R. and MATTHEWS, D. D. The grading of aggregates and workability of concrete, Road Research Technical Paper No. 5 (1947). London HMSO, pp. 38.
4. STEWART, D. A. *The Design and Placing of High Quality Concrete* (1962). London, Spon, pp. 162.
5. BRITISH STANDARDS INSTITUTION. Methods of testing concrete, Part 2—Methods of testing fresh concrete, BS 1881:Part 2:1970. London, British Standards Institution, pp. 35.
6. KEENE, P. W. A preliminary examination of the Vebe consistometer, Technical Report TRA/343 (November 1960). London, Cement and Concrete Association, pp. 13.
7. DEWAR, J. D. Relations between various workability control tests for ready-mixed concrete, Technical Report TRA/375 (February 1964). London, Cement and Concrete Association, pp. 17.
8. ROAD RESEARCH LABORATORY. Design of concrete mixes, Road Note No. 4, Second edition 1950 (reprinted 1958). London, HMSO, pp. 16.
9. MCINTOSH, J. D. and ERNTROY, H. C. The workability of concrete mixes with $\frac{3}{8}$-in aggregates, Research Report No. 2 (1955). London, Cement and Concrete Association, pp. 7.
10. KAPLAN, M. F. The effects of the properties of coarse aggregates on the workability of concrete, *Magazine of Concrete Research*, August 1958, **10,** No. 29, pp. 63–74.
11. BRITISH STANDARDS INSTITUTION. Methods for sampling and testing of mineral aggregates, sands and fillers, BS 812:1967. London, British Standards Institution, pp. 104.
12. SHERGOLD, F. A. The percentage voids in compacted gravel as a measure of its angularity, *Magazine of Concrete Research*, August 1953, **5,** No. 13, pp. 3–10.
13. MURDOCK, L. J. The workability of concrete, *Magazine of Concrete Research*, November 1960, **12,** No. 36, pp. 135–44.

14. BRITISH STANDARDS INSTITUTION. Specification for aggregates from natural sources for concrete (including granolithic), BS 882 and 1201:1965. London, British Standards Institution, pp. 22.
15. BRITISH STANDARDS INSTITUTION. Methods of testing concrete, Part 3—Methods of making and curing test specimens, BS 1881: Part 3:1970. London, British Standards Institution, pp. 25.
16. NEWMAN, K. The design of concrete mixes with high alumina cement, *The Reinforced Concrete Review,* March 1960, **5,** No. 5, pp. 269–301.
17. LEA, F. M. *The Chemistry of Cement and Concrete* (1970). London, Edward Arnold, pp. 727.
18. BRITISH STANDARDS INSTITUTION. Methods of testing concrete, Part 4—Methods of testing concrete for strength, BS 1881:Part 4:1970. London, British Standards Instititution, pp. 25.
19. PLOWMAN, J. M. Maturity and the strength of concrete, *Magazine of Concrete Research*, March 1956, **8,** No. 22, pp. 13–22.
20. OCKLESTON, A. J. *et al.* Discussion on Reference 19, *Magazine of Concrete Research*, November 1956, **8,** No. 24, pp. 173–83.
21. ANDREW, R. P. (Editor). Proceedings of a Symposium on Mix Design and Quality Control of Concrete, London, May 1954 (1955). London, Cement and Concrete Association, pp. 548.
22. NEWMAN, K. Concrete control tests as a measure of the properties of concrete, Proceedings of a Symposium on Concrete Quality, London, November 1964 (1966). London, Cement and Concrete Association, pp. 120–38.
23. ERNTROY, H. C. The variation of works test cubes, Research Report No. 10 (November 1960). London, The Cement and Concrete Association, pp. 28.
24. THE COUNCIL FOR CODES OF PRACTICE. Draft British Standard Code of Practice for the Structural Use of Concrete (1969). London, British Standards Institution, pp. 241.
25. BUILDING RESEARCH STATION. Concrete in sulphate-bearing soils and groundwater, Building Research Station Digest 90 (February 1968). Garston, Building Research Station, pp. 4.
26. ERNTROY, H. C. and SHACKLOCK, B. W. Design of high-strength concrete mixes, Proceedings of a Symposium on Mix Design and Quality Control of Concrete, London, May 1954 (1955). London, Cement and Concrete Association, pp. 55–73.
27. WRIGHT, P. J. F. Entrained air in Concrete, *Proceedings of the Institution of Civil Engineers,* May 1953, **2,** No. 3, pp. 337–58.
28. CORNELIUS, D. F. Air-entrained concretes: a survey of factors affecting air content and a study of concrete workability, RRL Report LR 363 (1970). Crowthorne, Road Research Laboratory, Ministry of Transport, pp. 18.
29. SHORT, A. and KINNIBURGH, W. Lightweight concrete (1963). London, Applied Science Publishers, pp. 368.
30. ACI COMMITTEE 613. Recommended practice for selecting proportions for structural lightweight concrete, ACI 613A–59 (1959). Detroit, American Concrete Institution, pp. 10.

31. Wright, P. J. F. The flexural strength of plain concrete; its measurement and use in designing concrete mixes, Road Research Technical Paper No. 67 (1964). London, HMSO, pp. 52.
32. Franklin, R. E. and King, T. M. J. Relations between compressive and indirect-tensile strengths of concrete, RRL Report LR 412 (1971). Crowthorne, Road Research Laboratory, Ministry of Transport, pp. 22.
33. Cornelius, D. F., Franklin, R. E. and King, T. M. J. The effect of test method on the indirect tensile strength of concrete, RRL Report LR 260 (1969). Crowthorne, Road Research Laboratory, Ministry of Transport, pp. 19.
34. Spooner, D. C. Measurement of the tensile strength of concrete by an indirect method—the cylinder splitting test, Technical Report TRA/419 (May 1969). London, Cement and Concrete Association, pp. 8.
35. Ministry of Transport. Specification for road and bridge works (1969). London, HMSO, pp. 195.

INDEX